No
Added
Sugar

No Added Sugar

growing up with type 1 diabetes

Fibi Ward

Hammersmith Press Ltd
London

First published in 2009 by Hammersmith Press Limited
496 Fulham Palace Road, London SW6 6JD, UK
www.hammersmithpress.co.uk

Whilst the advice and information in this book are believed to be true
and accurate at the date of going to press, neither the author nor the
publisher can accept any legal responsibility or liability for any errors or
omissions that may be made. In particular (but without limiting the gen-
erality of the preceding disclaimer) every effort has been made to check
drug dosages; however, it is still possible that errors may have been
missed. Furthermore, dosage schedules are particular to the individual
and are constantly being revised and new side effects recognized. For
these reasons readers are strongly urged to consult a health professional
with regard to their personal treatment regime.

British Library Cataloguing in Publication Data: A CIP record of this book
is available from the British Library.

ISBN 978-1-905140-26-8

Commissioning editor: Georgina Bentliff
Designed and typeset by Julie Bennett
Production by Helen Whitehorn, Pathmedia
Printed and bound by TJ International Ltd, Padstow, Cornwall, UK

Contents

A Huge Thank You ☺ ...

...to Mom and Dad, for everything but mostly for all your help and understanding in the last year – for not freaking out once even in the early days when I totally lost it – and for believing in me and my writing. You are the best parents ever. To Robert, my brother, for all your encouragement, especially at the beginning, and to everyone else in my family for all your support. You are all fab.

Also a massive thank you to my friends Poppy Bridgens, Hayley Butterworth, Abbie Clarke, Alice Crossley, Emma Harvell, Amber-Jean Morris, Charlotte Orbell and Samantha Wood – for all your support and understanding when I was first diagnosed and all your encouragement for my book too.

Thank you to Diane Cluley, my diabetes nurse – you have been an enormous help, both with checking my book and with all your help and advice since last year.

And finally, thank you to Georgina Bentliff, my publisher, for making it all possible.

Introduction

Before you start reading *No Added Sugar*, I think I should tell you a bit about why I decided to write it. I was diagnosed with type I diabetes in January 2008, when I was 13 years old. My diagnosis came completely out of the blue. I was shocked, scared, upset and confused all at the same time. I couldn't get my head around the fact that, from then on, I would have diabetes for the rest of my life, and I was dependent on having insulin injections every day.

Obviously, after I had been diagnosed, my parents and I had to get to grips with the treatment I was having; the more fully we understood my diabetes, the better we would be able to control it. We started looking for books that could help us find out about my condition. My parents wanted to read information books that would tell us all we needed to know about dealing with my diabetes – both the medical and practical aspects of it. They also wanted reassurance that however hard a time we were all going through at that moment, there was light at the end of the tunnel, and that, one day, I would be living a normal life again.

What *I* really wanted, however, was to read something by someone my own age, who knew and understood what I was going through. I didn't know anyone else who had type I diabetes, so there was no one I could talk to who had been through it themselves. Although some people will want to go to support groups and find them very helpful, I personally didn't want to go to one as I thought it would single me out even more as being 'different'. I felt I would rather find a book that I could relate to; knowing that there was someone else out there who was in the same boat as me would be really reassuring. I thought that I would get a lot of comfort from knowing I wasn't alone.

Although there are plenty of information books about diabetes, we couldn't see anything that we could relate to which focused on the psychological side of it – and we certainly didn't find anything by anyone my own age. I was going to have to come to terms with my diabetes without that help; that was what I tried to do.

At this point, I should perhaps add that, ever since I was very young, I've loved writing stories. From the age of about nine, my ambition has been to be a writer. I write stories (mostly teen fiction) in my spare time and first started sending them to publishers in 2007. In the March after my diagnosis, I had just finished writing my second 'book', and needed a new writing project to work on. Up until then, I'd forgotten about the seeming lack of books for diabetic teenagers like myself, and was getting on with my life the best I could. Then, almost out of nowhere, the idea came into my head that I could write about my diabetes. *Why not?* I thought. I could at least have a go at it. So, that evening, I began writing what has now become this book.

No Added Sugar is not a medical book. It doesn't focus on the clinical side of type 1 diabetes, but on the emotional, social and practical aspects of living your life with it. Any medical information I have included has been checked by my diabetes nurse; however, the medical side of diabetes is not the main point. My book is about my experiences of coming to terms with diabetes, the feelings I have been through after being diagnosed and the practical advice that I can offer from my own experience.

Writing *No Added Sugar* has been extremely rewarding, occasionally emotional and, in some ways, quite therapeutic. I've come a long way since I first started it; reading my book back a year on, I've realised that there were lots of things that I'd completely forgotten I'd been so worried about. If I'd started writing now rather than last year, this would be a completely different book – which just shows that it *is* possible to get back to normal after being diagnosed with diabetes.

You may be going through situations like the ones I have been through – or your experiences may be completely different. But the feelings that you have will be in some way similar to those I had. Accepting your diabetes is a difficult readjustment, but in time you will be able to get used to it. I hope that this book will help you to make that transition.

Basically, this is the book that I wanted to read when I was first diagnosed. I hope you find it useful. If you are scared, shocked, sad, angry, confused, frustrated, embarrassed or worried about your diabetes then this book is for you, and I hope that by reading *No Added Sugar*, you can gain some comfort and reassurance – you are not alone.

Fibi Ward
2009

1
In shock

10th January 2008

"Dear diary,
"I'm writing this in a bed in ward 1 at the Alexandra
Hospital because I have been diagnosed. I have to stay
overnight. The injections hurt. Blood tests aren't that bad.
The thumb prick was the worst."

When I was first diagnosed with type 1 diabetes, it was terrifying. To begin with, I couldn't even face writing in my own private diary exactly what I had been diagnosed with. I could never imagine life carrying on as normal ever again.

I was lucky, though, because I had never been ill with my diabetes before we knew about it. The nurse said that children are often very ill by the time they go into hospital, but the only symptom I had had was a horrible, unquenchable thirst. This meant that hopefully I wouldn't have to stay in hospital for very long at all. Even so, I was scared about the prospect of an overnight stay in hospital, especially as I had hardly ever set foot in one before as a visitor, let alone as a patient.

I can remember almost every moment of my short stay in hospital quite vividly. Having been referred to the paediatric ward by my GP, I arrived, aged 13, at the Alexandra Hospital with my parents at about half past two on the 10th January 2008. I knew nothing about diabetes; it hadn't even been confirmed that it was diabetes yet. The nurses on the ward were very friendly and reassuring. I was shown to my bed on the empty 'Bay C' and I was measured, weighed and asked a lot of questions about my medical background and my family's medical history. I didn't understand how I could have diabetes when there was no family history of it.

Later, we met the dietician and diabetes nurse, and the paediatric consultant. We met so many different people and were given so much information; my mind was boggling from information overload.

Throughout my whole time in hospital, I was in shock. My mind had gone blurry and everything was fuzzy and surreal. I felt like I was acting in a play of someone else's life – like, "Who wants to play the girl with diabetes?"... and I'd got picked. Probably because my mind had been temporarily numbed by the whole thing, I didn't really care that much what happened about my diabetes; like I said, it was someone else's life anyway – and the only thing that was really real was the pain of my first injections.

Finding out I had diabetes was frightening and surreal and also sad, but parts of my stay in hospital, strange as it seems, were actually quite funny. Mom was allowed to stay overnight with me on the ward, sleeping in a fold-out bed next to mine. When I was tired and ready for bed we pulled the hanging curtains around our little part of the bay. I lay in bed looking around. The curtains surrounding us were like the walls of a tent; the children's ward was just a strange new place to explore. It hadn't sunk in why I was there – it was almost like a long dream, one of those dreams that make sense while you're there but then you wake up wondering what on earth it was all about. I was half-expecting a herd of flying pigs to come crashing in through the window, and then for the hospital to dissolve away into thin air and leave me sitting up in my own bed back at home.

The next morning, all the doctors came in to the bay to talk to Mom and me. I remember we had made a huge list of questions to ask, and they were answering all of them very honestly and giving us lots of information. It was hard to take it all seriously, though, when all I could concentrate on was my Mom's fringe sticking up on end like a cockatoo's crest!

I was discharged from hospital that evening. My leg was still aching from my second dose of Lantus (glargine) and as I walked to the car it was already dark. I can't explain why, but the drive home felt like the Great Escape from diabetes. If only I could leave it at the hospital…

When I was back at home, everything went crazy. It all continued to feel surreal and everything was still fuzzy and confusing. I still didn't feel like I was living my own life – the only explanation that made any vague sort of sense was that I was in a back-to-front world where nothing was the same any more. My parents became Mommy and Daddy again, even though I hadn't called them that since I was about ten, and my life was dominated by injections – mealtimes seemed to blur into each other because I found it so difficult to cope with injections so I took ages every time I ate. (My insulin regime was – and still is – a multiple-injection one, with four injections a day: one Novorapid (aspart) injection with every meal and a background Lantus (glargine) insulin at about teatime).

If you have just been diagnosed...

- If you are newly diagnosed with diabetes and feel like your life is revolving around it, try not to get stressed out (although sometimes this can be much easier said than done).

- Your diabetes seems to be taking priority at the moment because it's all new to you and your family. Try to accept that things are changing – whether you like it or not – and remember that you *will* get past the phase where everything is new and scary. You *will* soon be able to carry on with your normal day-to-day life – and you'll be surprised at how quickly this happens.

• Your family don't have to come to terms with diabetes in the same way that you have to, but it is a big shock for them too. You may find that your parents become more protective of you, or that younger brothers or sisters are put out because they feel that you're getting more attention than normal and they're losing out. Whichever way, family life will soon settle back to normal as you all see the reality of it and work out how much you can do for yourself and which responsibilities still lie with your parents.

2
Early worries

As soon as I was told that I might have diabetes, a load of questions started whizzing around in my head. Was I going to die? Was there anything I could have done to stop it? How could I have this when no one else in my family had it? Would I have to take medication? Wasn't diabetes caused by being fat? Was I fat, then? I felt insulted that I could have something wrong with me. Did it mean I was faulty? Was I disabled? I'd always taken it for granted that I was perfectly healthy and didn't need any sort of medication to keep me well. I felt ashamed at the thought that I might be ill. I didn't feel ill. I wasn't looking forward to a life of dependency on hospitals and medication. Would I be in and out of a doctor's surgery all the time? Might I as well go ahead and move into a hospital permanently? But I didn't feel ill! How could I be?

Mom told me that even if I did have diabetes, it didn't mean I was *ill*. It would mean that I had a medical condition, but one that could be treated and kept under control. I could still have a normal life, if I was careful and took whatever treatment I had to. But that wasn't my idea of a normal life. I wanted to be fit and healthy like everyone else, not needing to take any medication. I had thought there could never be anything wrong with me, I could never be seriously ill and I would never have to rely on anything.

Although it was a big shock when it was confirmed at the hospital, I didn't cry nearly as much or feel as upset as when the GP first mentioned the word "diabetes". I think it was because I'd been numbed by the original shock of thinking that I might have diabetes, and had sort of subconsciously prepared myself for the worst.

Now a new swarm of questions was buzzing around in my mind. Would I still be able to go to a normal school? Would my friends think differently of me? Would I be bullied about it? Would my teachers feel sorry for me? Could I pretend it wasn't happening? No one would have to know, would they? How could I keep it a secret? It was all pretty terrifying. But I think the worst thing was fear of the unknown.

Lots of my questions were answered over the course of the next two days. I could still go to school with my friends, and I could still learn to drive, and get a job, and I would be able to lead a normal life. The doctors and nurses were very helpful and told me everything I needed to know about the practical side of dealing with my new condition, but there were some more personal questions that I knew they just wouldn't be able to answer, many I didn't even want to ask.

I was scared to go back to school in case anyone bullied me, and I so hated the thought that my photo would have to go up in the staffroom at school, so that all the teachers would know who I was and what was the matter with me. I cringed at the idea of it, almost like I had my photo on the wall of shame, like I was one on the list of poor wretched kids who had something wrong with them. I was capable of looking after myself; I neither needed nor wanted some well-meaning supply teacher pitying me as the poor girl who has to stab needles in her stomach every time she eats. I'd been told enough times that it was important for my teachers to know, but I still didn't understand just why every member of staff in the school had to know about me. That wasn't my idea of a normal life.

And I was resolute that nobody in my classes apart from my very best friends would ever find out. This wasn't just because I was scared that some of the nasty gangs of girls would pick on me; I was worried that no boys would ever want to go out with me if they knew. I felt like an alien at the thought of going back now I was suddenly diabetic, like I would never fit back in amongst happy, healthy people who had no idea what I'd been through.

Questions you're probably asking yourself

- **"Will I be bullied?"** – It's unlikely. Obviously, I can't say for certain, but from my experience a lot of people are a lot more understanding than you might expect. Diabetes is nothing to be embarrassed or ashamed of, it doesn't make you any different as a person to anybody else, and there is nothing about it to be made fun of – so, if you are bullied, remember that yes, you have diabetes, but you also have a life – something they need to get. Bullying you for the fact that you need injections is just sad behaviour from sad people.

- **"How do I tell people?"** – Be casual about it. You probably don't want to go out of your way to tell people unless you have to, so wait until they ask you about it. A good opportunity to get it off your chest (if you're feeling brave) is when you first go back to school after being diagnosed. People will probably ask you why you have been off, which can be really daunting if you feel like you don't want to tell people – but, if you'd rather get it out of the way then answer their questions honestly. Don't let other people see that it's a big deal to you – if you're matter-of-fact about it, they will be too. You don't have to tell anyone about it until you're ready to, but what is a cue to put people right is if you hear any rumours coming back to you; when I first went back to school after I was diagnosed, one of my friends told me that she'd overheard someone saying that they thought I was pregnant! I don't know where that came from, but keeping a big secret and getting flustered if any-one tried to ask me about why I had been off must have started somebody's imagination going… So it really is better that people know the truth to start with.

- **"How will people react?"** - It depends. Some people will gasp and stare like you told them that you were nearly murdered last night and some people will look blankly at you as though you told them you're having fish and chips for tea. From my experience, lots of people will be much more understanding than you might expect, and say something like, "Oh, my auntie/cousin/friend's got diabetes too". If you do get a funny reaction from somebody, don't be offended - remember that it's more than likely because they simply don't understand what diabetes is.

- **"How will I do my injections at school?"** – In time, it won't be a big deal at all. If you are on a multiple-injection regime, then when you are confident with doing your injections, you will be able to stay at school for lunch and do your lunchtime injection there. It may work differently at your school, but this is how I do my lunchtime Novorapid (aspart) at my school: my insulin is kept in a locked cupboard in the medical room. (I carry my glucose meter with me in my blazer pocket.) I take my blood sugar at the table before I eat, then once I have finished my lunch I go to the medical room. The First Aider (who has the key to the cupboard) gets my insulin from the cupboard and makes a note of my blood sugar and how many units of insulin I am having. Then I do my injection in the medical room. Nobody else has to come in the room whilst I am doing the injection, except for the First Aider who is there to make sure there are no problems. I then leave my insulin at school. Obviously this only applies if you are on a multiple-injection regime; if you are only doing two injections a day then you will not need to inject in school.

3
Before we knew

I was lucky because I was never ill with my diabetes before we found out about it. The only symptom that I noticed was that I became extremely thirsty. I could never quench my thirst; sometimes I would go into the kitchen and drink five or six whole cups of juice – and even then I would only stop because I felt too waterlogged to drink any more.

I can remember vividly one occasion when my thirst drove me to despair – I had literally just eaten dinner (with three cups of apple juice) and was sitting upstairs at my desk trying to finish a piece of homework. After only a few minutes, I started to feel thirsty. I told myself that I would finish my homework and then go and get a drink. But my thirst got stronger, and I only managed to write a couple more sentences before I had to pop downstairs to get some milk.

I poured myself a cup full to the brim with milk, took one sip and told myself to take the rest upstairs to drink while I finished my homework. Yet as soon as I had swallowed that sip, I had to take another one. Only I ended up drinking a massive gulp of milk, and then the rest of the cup in ten seconds or so. I still felt desperately thirsty.

I poured myself half a cup of milk and drank it in one go, then another whole cup to take upstairs. But I had to stop half way up the stairs to drink that. I was still gagging for another drink, but my stomach felt so full I knew I couldn't take much more. So I got myself another cup of milk and managed to get it upstairs. I sat down at my desk, picked up my pen, wrote one sentence and then dropped my pen and gulped back all the milk.

Afterwards I felt sick, bloated and completely waterlogged, but still thirsty. I was angry with myself – what was the matter with me? That piece of homework – only about four short paragraphs – ended up taking the best part of three hours. Half an hour of that was writing, fifteen minutes thinking and around about two hours in and out of the kitchen and bathroom.

Now that I know more about the symptoms of diabetes, I can look back and see that, actually, I had more symptoms too. There were a few times when I really struggled to breathe, and my eyes sometimes used to go blurry.

Recognising the symptoms

- The most commonly associated symptom of diabetes is extreme thirst, like I experienced. The reason you become more thirsty is that your body is trying to flush the excess sugar out of your system by taking in more water.

- As a result of this, you may need to use the toilet more often, especially during the night.

- Blurred vision can also be a sign of diabetes. This is because glucose from the blood is transported to the optical lens by fluid (aqueous humour) within the eye. When the glucose concentration of the optical lens is higher than that of the blood, the lens absorbs water from the eye which causes it (the lens) to swell; this in turn causes the rays of light passing through the lens into the eye to be distorted, resulting in a blurred image being seen. Think of this as a similar effect to looking out of a frosted glass window and seeing a distorted image (as with high blood sugar) compared with looking through a clear glass window and seeing a sharp image (as with normal blood sugar).

- Also, if you have untreated diabetes you can end up losing weight. This is because, while there is no insulin to let the sugar from the blood into the cells, the cells are being starved of energy and therefore send out signals to break down the body's fat stores into sugar for energy. This results in even more sugar in the blood, continuing a vicious cycle; and furthermore, ketones, which are produced when fats are broken down into sugars, build up in the body – which can go on to cause ketoacidosis (a rare but serious illness associated with high blood sugar levels) if you are not treated with insulin injections.

- On top of this, untreated diabetes can cause you to become tired due to the lack of energy getting to the cells in your body.

4
Back to school

I went back to school after a week, when a care plan had been put in place for me. I found this a very difficult and stressful step, as I was hypersensitive about my diabetes and didn't want anyone except my best friends to know about it. I was worried that the process of re-adjusting my school life to include looking after my diabetes would change everything that I was used to and make me feel like the odd one out; plus I didn't know how everyone at school – my friends, teachers and classmates – would react to the fact that I was suddenly diabetic and whether they would treat me any differently. I even felt embarrassed about my diabetes. I told my friends everything, but I swore them to secrecy and was adamant that nobody else would find out. I wasn't denying what was happening – but I couldn't get it into my head that I couldn't send my diabetes back after the 30-day trial was up. I thought that if nobody else knew, my life might be able to somehow revert back to how it had been before. It was like, by telling someone, I'd make what I was saying real. I still didn't think this was actually my life; it just seemed like a long, vivid, crazy nightmare.

If you are worried about school...

- When you first go back to school after being diagnosed, it's only normal to feel a bit nervous, or even really scared.

- Don't tell anyone anything that you don't want to, but...

- It is a good idea to tell a few friends so that they know what's going on and can look out for you if you have any problems.

- A care plan will be put in place at school. This means arranging a quiet, private place where you can go to do your injections, but also informing all of your teachers that you may need to eat during lessons if your blood sugar goes low, and making sure you will be able to have exercise snacks during P.E.

5
Cat's out of the bag

For the first couple of weeks at school, I went home at lunchtimes as I was still struggling with my Novorapid (aspart) injections. In the space of those two weeks, I had improved enormously with my mealtime injections (my diabetes nurse introduced me to the Pen-Mate* (manufactured by Novonordisk), a gadget which I found very helpful as it stopped me being so hesitant to do the injections). After another week, I was ready to stay in school to have my insulin.

My class had a new teacher for one subject, and two lessons a week with the new teacher were immediately before lunch. However, her lessons often ran into lunchtime – and I needed to use my lunchtime to eat, take my blood sugar reading and have my injection. One of the perks was that I was allowed to leave as soon as the lunch bell went.

But on the first lesson with the teacher, as I was about to go to lunch, she started to discuss my insulin with me - and at a volume such that my friend sitting over the other side of the classroom picked up the key words of "Matron" and "injection". Having kept my diabetes confined to strict secrecy for nearly a month, and

(* The PenMate is a gadget that hides the needle so you can't see it go into the skin. It also puts the needle into the skin for you – you pull back the base of the pen, rest the PenMate against your injection site and press a button which puts the needle in in a split second, so that you don't have to put it off for ages while you try to psych yourself up for it.)

still feeling insecure about it myself, I was absolutely mortified that she had basically told the whole class. She had no right whatsoever to discuss my personal, confidential medical information in front of anyone, let alone thirty other students.

I left the classroom, slamming the door behind me and running down the stairs to the dinner hall in tears. She'd basically spelt it out to the whole class – I was infuriated. What would everyone think now they knew I had diabetes? I had no idea how they would react; I didn't know who knew what, either. I felt angrier than I can remember feeling ever before, like the ground was opening up below me and I was falling into a pit of helplessness because I had no control over who knew what.

When I got home, I told my parents what had happened; I was getting really stressed, and I was dreading going to school again in case anyone mentioned it to me or took the mickey. Mom and Dad were angry about it too - Mom went in to speak to a senior teacher and explained what had happened and how distressed I was.

Who has to know?

- Teachers are only told on a need-to-know basis – this means they are only told because they absolutely have to know.

- It's important that at least one or two friends know from the start, so they can understand that you may have to take blood tests, treat hypoglycaemia or hyperglycaemia or have snacks at certain times. Also, when you go to your friends' houses, it will be a lot easier if they understand that you'll need to do injections when you eat – and, fairly soon if not yet (especially so if you're on a multiple-injection regime or insulin pump), you'll have to calculate the carbohydrate content of all your meals from carb counting books or food packaging – much easier when someone can help you find all the packets and tins.

• However, your diabetes is your business, not anyone else's – you have a right to keep it private if you would really rather no one else knew.

• On the other hand, it will be much easier in the long run if people know about your diabetes. The longer it stays a secret, the bigger deal it is to tell people – and you may even find that people start inventing their own explanations for the things you have to do if they don't know the true reason behind it.

• My advice is not to tell anyone about your diabetes if you don't feel comfortable with telling them. It's perfectly understandable not to want your medical condition to be common knowledge – but, as you come to terms with it, you will probably find you don't mind telling people who ask, and from my experience, it is much, much easier if you do.

6
Misunderstanding

It turned out that not many people had actually picked up on what the teacher had said. But the following day, she said something else in front of the class. I was really annoyed by this and in the heat of the moment, I decided I'd had enough and asked if I could have a word with her outside the classroom.

"Miss, I don't know whether you realise it," I started, slightly nervous because I wasn't sure how she'd react, "but you've – well, you've sort of told everyone about me having diabetes. I mean, what you've discussed in front of everyone else, that's my personal information, and I don't want anyone else to know that."

Then she argued, "But in a way, it's better if everyone does know about it." She said that if I passed out in one of her lessons, it would scare the other pupils in the class and she would have no time to answer questions and reassure them that I would be okay. From what she said, I gathered that she also thought that I would pass out at the drop of a hat if my blood sugar went low or high. I soon realised that by discussing my diabetes in front of other people, she wasn't trying to be spiteful or irritating; it all stemmed from ignorance – and that wasn't really the teacher's fault.

I began to see things from her perspective. I realised she hadn't upset me intentionally; she had just never thought that what she was saying would bother me. I calmed down a bit and explained to her that I was extremely unlikely to pass out. I assured her that I could usually recognise the signs as soon as I started to go hypo and would be able to treat it easily by myself, without needing to leave the classroom or even make it obvious what I was doing. I said that my friends did know, but at that moment, they were the only people I wanted to know about it.

The teacher said that she understood that I was upset and apologised for what she'd done. I realised she really hadn't known at the time that she was doing anything wrong.

I was much happier after that, realising there was no way she had done it to be nasty. I haven't had any other occasions like this since - to be honest, she was actually very supportive and understanding for the rest of the year if I ever needed to do blood tests or treat hypos in her lessons.

If this happens to you...

You should not have any problems at school with your teachers, but if you ever find yourself in the same situation as I was, there are a few ways that you can deal with it:

- Try speaking to the teacher. They may not understand what they have done wrong.

- If this doesn't work, or you feel too awkward to speak to them face-to-face, then tell your parents or someone else who you trust who might be able to help you. Explain how you feel and ask them if they could speak to the teacher for you, or go with you to see another member of staff to report the incident.

- And remember that, although you may not feel ready to tell people about your diabetes yet, it really is easier in the long run if people know. They are going to find out at some point.

• If a teacher does 'let it out' as happened to me, put the incident in a positive light; say that at least you didn't have to stress about how to tell people.

7
Realisation

After a few weeks, it began to sink in that I was stuck with diabetes. There was no 30-day trial and I couldn't send it back. My days of being carefree were over before they had really begun. Like: happy, happy, happy, not a care in the world. Then: diabetes, doom, gloom. Carefree days going, going, gone.

I was fed up with – well, everything. I hadn't chosen to be landed with it. I didn't want to have to have it. I was sick of it. I started to feel down every time I had to do an injection. It all seemed so unfair. Why me? Why did I have to do this? I'd had enough. I considered starving myself so that I didn't have to have any mealtime injections. I thought about just not taking insulin, full stop. I'd managed for over twelve years without them, so why did I need injections now? I seriously wondered about forgetting I had diabetes, maybe just for a couple of weeks, just to give myself a break from it. Once I felt so frustrated with everything that I started punching my arm to let my anger out.

I used to feel like I was a different person. I wasn't Fibi any more, I was Diabetic Fibi. I defined myself by the fact that I had diabetes, and thought that other people who knew would too. I felt like I was two different people: myself before diabetes and myself after diabetes. I desperately wanted to go back to the "other me". It was almost like I had been at a point where I came to a dead end and the only way I could carry on and grow up and get on with my life was to go through the rest of it with my new condition. But how-ever much I hated the idea of staying 13 forever, I thought I would much rather do that and always be a normal teenager than grow up hampered by diabetes. Yet I knew that, besides anything else, it was *impossible* for me to just stop at 13 and stay on the border of 'diabetic-ness'. It was like I had just been thrown into the deep end with no warning that my life would be suddenly disrupted by the onset of an unwanted medical condition. To start with I was too shocked to feel upset or angry about it. It was a few weeks after my diagnosis that I realised this was reality – and it came like a punch in the face.

If you feel down about everything...

It may be hard when you're trapped in a negative frame of mind to put everything into perspective and think positively, but you have to, or else you'll get dragged into a vicious cycle and feel much worse. So, how can you pull yourself out of it and carry on with stuff?

- Talk to someone about it. A problem shared is a problem halved – it's such an old cliché but it is true. When you feel it's an appropriate time, have a good chat to a parent or another close relative about your diabetes. Don't wait until you're tearing your hair out over it to discuss your feelings with someone – talking about it the next time you're a bit sad will help your relative to understand how you feel and what you're worried or upset about. Also, saying what's bothering you out loud can help to put it into perspective – it seems such a huge problem when it's bottled up inside you, but when you get it out in the open you realise that what's been eating away at you might really not be that much of a big deal in the whole scheme of things.

- Don't be afraid to cry. Trying to kid yourself that you're not really upset about anything may work for some people, but it'll do more harm than good for others. Be honest with yourself – if you feel angry or miserable then recognise this and find a way to get over it and move on. You might think that crying will make you a baby, but if it helps you to let your feelings out and move on then go with it.

- Let your anger out – but try to do something constructive rather than destructive. Don't storm about slamming things around or, even worse, don't be tempted to take it out on yourself by hurting yourself. Instead, maybe try keeping a diary, writing in it how angry you are and having a real rant about everything that's on your mind. Or, if keeping a diary isn't your thing, just write down what's bothering you on a scrap of paper and then throw it on the fire or run it through a shredder. Also, although it's good to talk to people about the way you feel, be conscious that you don't make it seem like you're taking it out on them. Remember that it's nobody's fault – blaming yourself or anyone else is neither reasonable nor helpful.

8
Facing the facts

I didn't like doing blood tests, and at times I *hated* doing my injections – but I could cope with them. The thing that really scared me was the fact that I *had* to do them. But for the first few weeks I just thought that without my insulin I would develop more symptoms, lose weight, feel unwell, become a frail, skinny little thing who was always ill with something – and I thought that was all that could happen to me. I knew it was important to have my injections, but I didn't understand just how important it was.

Until... "Do you think there was anyone with type 1 diabetes on the Titanic?" Dad asked me, reading from a book.

I hesitated. Quite a few people were diabetic, so there must have been, mustn't there? "Um, yes?"

Dad shook his head thoughtfully, looking back at the book. Then he said, "No. Insulin hadn't been discovered at the time of the Titanic, so anyone who had type 1 diabetes would have died within months."*

I suddenly realised the implications of this – if anyone who had diabetes would be dead within months, that meant that without my insulin I would only have... Well, we think my diabetes started in September-ish of the year before I was diagnosed... Which meant

*(Insulin was discovered in 1921 by Dr Frederick Banting and Charles Best. It was first used to treat humans in 1922).

I was supposed to be dead by now. No! That couldn't be right. I wasn't supposed to be here? I was meant to have died already? No way! Not me. Why me? *Why me?*

It came as a terrible shock, so much so that I went and cried for hours afterwards. But Mom put the situation in a different light.

"Would you worry about what could happen to you if you were alive in Victorian times, because there were more diseases going around then that could have killed people?" she asked.

"Of course I'd worry about being in Victorian times, *now* – I'd be dead!"

I saw what she meant, though. It's true, not many people spend their time worrying about whether they would have caught the Black Death if they had been around at that time, or been thrown to the lions in the time of the Roman Empire. It's irrelevant. You are not a Victorian, an ancient Roman or a villager in the 1600s. You're alive here and now, where insulin has been discovered and Man has landed on the moon and they are getting ever-closer to a cure for diabetes. So there's no point getting upset because you know where you'd be without insulin – as long as you take it, it's irrelevant.

If you hear things that scare you...

There will be times when you read things that might really frighten or upset you. We can't deny facts, but there are a few things to ask yourself before you panic:

- **Who has written it?** Information from unreliable sources can be exaggerated or inaccurate. Don't believe rumours or "shock-horror" stories unless they come from a reputable information source.

- **Why is it there?** Websites, articles and programmes can mention diabetes for a whole range of reasons. An article on a website for people who have diabetes would probably use positive statistics to reassure them. But an article as part of a charity campaign will probably use negative statistics to grab people's attention and make them feel something has to be done. Campaigns purposefully pick the most shocking facts and figures to persuade people to donate, so remember that any scary news stories you hear relating to diabetes awareness or fundraising are usually worst-case scenarios.

- **What does it actually mean?** Don't take statistics at face value. If a statistic seems unrealistic, there could be a hidden twist to it. For example, the figure "50% of people with diabetes" will include people with type 1 *and* type 2 diabetes, and "twice as likely" could only be a tiny increase in probability if the chance to start with was something like one in a thousand.

- **Is it relevant?** If you go looking for facts and figures, you'll stumble across something that upsets you. It's almost certain. But some of the things you read could be incorrect or exaggerated, and mean nothing anyway. And even if a fact is unarguably correct, it can probably be put into perspective – like my worry mentioned above. Just don't go looking for statistics and don't take notice of everything you see.

9
First injections

While I was in hospital, I picked up on how to do my injections really quickly. However, when I got back home, I suddenly lost my confidence and was really reluctant to have my insulin. After one dinnertime, I actually took nearly an hour to have my Lantus (glargine).

Mom spoke to my diabetes nurse, who then showed me the PenMate (mentioned earlier), which helped me to overcome this. I also found that holding an ice pack on the part of my leg or stomach where I was going to inject helped with my mealtime insulin. However, I realised that with the Lantus (glargine), this actually makes it sting more.

I sometimes hit a nerve or a blood vessel when I have my injections. When I hit a blood vessel it is usually slightly painful for the first few seconds, then the pain stops, but the injection site often feels sore or achy after I take the needle out, and there is a drop of blood on the skin where a vein has been pierced. Occasionally, I also get a little bruise after a few days where I have hit a blood vessel. When I hit a nerve, it is always very intensely painful - but normally only for the 10 seconds while the needle is in. I've also learnt that when I have my Lantus (glargine), it isn't uncommon to feel a burning pain which quickly goes after all the insulin has been injected. This is apparently nothing to do with the actual needle itself, but it is the insulin that hurts because Lantus (glargine) insulin is more acidic than Novorapid (aspart).

We have also discovered that the Opticlick pen (for the Lantus (glargine)) switches itself off after a certain amount of time; this did cause lots of problems when I used to be really hesitant to inject - we were sometimes unsure whether the insulin had been injected.

As well, I've found out that it is possible to test whether there is a nerve in the place that you're about to put the needle (and this works with whichever insulin you are using). This is done by gently touching the tip of the needle against the surface of the skin; if you feel a sharp pain then it is likely that there is a nerve there. If it doesn't hurt, there is most likely no nerve there and at this point I carry on and push the needle into the skin.

Although this method usually finds where there are nerves, there have been times when there has been a nerve that this little test hasn't picked up on. In these instances, you must decide before pressing the button in whether you can bear the pain for 10 seconds. It's really important not to inject the insulin if you can't hold the needle in for a count of 10; this may result in an incorrect dose

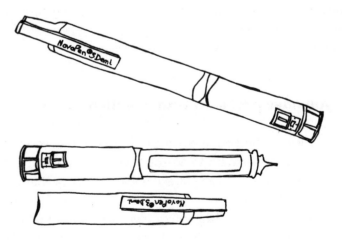

being given and going hyper later on. If you're not sure if you'll be able to keep the needle in for 10 seconds, it's best to take it out and start again – of course, there's no guarantee that the same thing won't happen again.

If, after repeating this process three or four times, I still haven't managed to inject, then I tell myself that I will try one more time, and if I still haven't had my insulin, I will just put the needle in some-where and stick with it – and then I make sure that I do. If you do this you will find it may hurt (a lot) at the time, but it will be easier in the long run as it will prevent you from getting stressed out or frustrated with yourself when you're still trying to do an injection half an hour later.

One thing I will say, as strange as it may sound: I feel like the pain is not quite as much as when I first started taking insulin. That is to say that I have got used to it. I remember that the Lantus (glargine) really did used to sting, every time I did this injection, but now it really doesn't seem painful. Also, when I used to hit nerves not long after I was diagnosed, I would often feel that the only way to help relieve the pain while the needle was in was to cry out or grimace. Now I think I am a lot better at coping with painful injec-tions, as I haven't felt the need to scream "ouch!" for quite a while (by the way I'm talking about *very* painful injections).

If you have problems with injections...

- Insulin injections aren't the best thing in the world – they can be awkward to do, you have to carry a load of extra stuff when you go out, and, above all, they can hurt.

- But the worst thing you can do is to put them off, because this will cause you to get frustrated with yourself and make the whole experience more unpleasant than it has to be.

- You have to have your injection, but you *don't* have to spend half an hour getting psyched up and stressed out. It does feel very unnatural to poke a needle into your skin, but don't keep telling yourself that you shouldn't have to do it. Instead, tell yourself that by having an injection, you are doing the best possible thing you can for yourself – your injections keep you well. Or, best of all, don't tell yourself anything, and just get it over and done with.

- If you're worried you'll slip with the needle and hurt yourself, get your mom, dad, or an older brother or sister to hold the hand that you're doing your injection with and help to guide the needle in.

- And if all else fails, you can always ask your mom or dad to do the injections for you to start with.

10
Hypos

When I was told about hypos at the hospital, I was a bit scared. I didn't know when my first hypo was going to happen, or what I would feel like when it did, and I was dreading it.

To begin with, my blood sugar readings were often good, but I did regularly have hypos (around two or three a week). Going hypo wasn't as bad as I'd imagined. My vision would sometimes become disturbed (e.g. the colours of things would appear to keep changing – this is not to be confused with blurred vision from a high sugar level) and I sometimes felt light-headed. As time has gone on, however, I've found that the symptoms I get have changed in phases; at the start I would always get disturbed vision and light-headedness, then I used to feel shaky and light-headed, and now I usually feel tired, shaky and sick.

My first night-time hypo with symptoms was a horrible experience. Before I went to bed, my blood sugar was 4.8 mmol/l – this was a bit low before bedtime, so I had an extra biscuit with my bedtime snack to try to bring it up a little bit. (The normal range for someone without diabetes is 4-7 mmol/l; for someone with diabetes, the target range is normally either 4-10 mmol/l or 4-8 mmol/l.) After I had eaten my bedtime snack, I took my blood sugar again; this time it had gone up to 10.2 mmol/l. I then went to bed as normal.

In the night, I had really horrible nightmares. I remember waking up a couple of times in the early hours of the morning and really not feeling right but then I must have fallen straight back to sleep again.

In the morning, my mom had to wake me up for school – I was so tired! I could hardly open my eyes and I just lay there, even though Mom was nudging me and telling me I had to get up. I felt weak and exhausted and my arms and legs were shaky. I felt hypo, but I was too tired to sit up and do a blood test. Mom got my glucose meter from downstairs and brought it up to me. She took my blood sugar for me – I had tried to get the test strip out of the packet, but my hands were so weak and shaky that it just slipped around in my fingers.

My blood sugar was 6.3 mmol/l, but I felt so bad that we knew I must have gone hypo in the middle of the night and my blood sugar had brought itself back up. I couldn't go into school – I could barely sit up. I stayed at home until just after break time, by which point I felt okay.

A few weeks later, I woke up in the middle of the night again with my arms feeling shaky. I was convinced I was hypo, but I was so tired that I fell back to sleep. It wasn't until the morning that I found out there had been an earth tremor in the night. So much for a hypo!

Tips on hypos

- If you feel sick or dizzy or have disturbed vision or recognise any other hypo symptoms, do a blood test straight away. It is much easier to treat a hypo of 3.9 mmol/l than wait until you are at 2 mmol/l and feeling very unwell.

- If you have found that you are hypo and have taken dextrose tablets or another suitable form of sugar, wait for at least a few minutes before taking another blood test. Dextrose does not act instantaneously and you could end up thinking that your hypo is getting worse when actually it will be on the way up within a minute or two.

• When you have had a few hypos, you should start to recognise what the typical signs are. Many people experience light-headedness, disturbed vision, going pale, shaking, extreme hunger, severe tiredness or nausea when they are hypo. These are the classic symptoms, but not everyone will get all or even any of these; in the same way, you may get symptoms which are not the general ones but which you learn to recognise as a sign that your blood sugar levels are low. Basically, with experience you should learn to pick up on the early signs of a hypo before you feel too unwell.

11
P.E.

P.E. has, for obvious reasons, proved the most problematic lesson as far as my blood sugar is concerned. On several occasions, I have overestimated the amount of exercise snacks needed and ended up going hyper. I have also managed to keep my blood sugar normal during and just after P.E., but then sometimes it has gone low – hypo

or in the low fours (see later in this chapter) in the evening after a P.E. lesson. In fact, the time when I had my first bad night-time hypo was after a P.E. lesson. I have found that immediately after P.E., my blood sugar tends to be slightly higher than it should be (10-12 mmol/l) and it has sometimes gone up to 15 mmol/l, but very quickly (within 10 minutes) gone back to 7 or 8 mmol/l. In the half hour or so after P.E., my blood sugar sometimes falls very quickly to around 5 mmol/l. (Normal blood sugar for a person without diabetes stays within the range of 4-7 mmol/l. If you have diabetes then your target range is usually either 4-10 mmol/l or 4-7 mmol/l.)

When you do P.E....

- If you're worried about your blood sugar during P.E., you can always go to your school's first aider for help.

- You can still do after-school sports clubs, too, as long as you plan for them and take exercise snacks like you do for P.E.

- If you are worried about people finding out about your diabetes, you may not want other people to see you eating an exercise snack in case they ask why you are eating it. Dextrose tablets are a good alternative, as you can take them quite discreetly so nobody notices and questions you.

- Don't worry about being told off for eating an exercise snack; your P.E. teacher will know that you have diabetes and should allow you to eat and take blood glucose tests when you need to.

- Match your exercise snack to the type of exercise you are doing. For instance, aerobics or sprinting uses lots of energy and a good exercise snack would be dextrose or a sugary drink – whereas an exercise snack with a slightly lower Glycaemic Index such as chocolate, is more suitable for gentler exercise like rounders or basketball. (The Glycaemic Index (G.I.) is a ranking of foods in terms of how quickly their carbohydrate content gets into the bloodstream as glucose. Low G.I. foods, for example pasta, take a long time to break down into glucose and have a less profound effect on blood sugar levels; whereas high G.I. foods, like sugary sweets, get into the blood very quickly and cause a much greater peak in blood glucose.)

• Finally, when you start eating chocolate, sweets or sugary foods as an exercise snack, there is always the temptation to have more. Try not to use P.E. as an excuse to eat more sweets than you really need. You may end up going hyper afterwards and feeling ill, so it really isn't worth it just for one sweet or chocolate.

12
Sweets, treats and choco-mania

Just because you have diabetes doesn't mean you have to go without sweets and desserts. My experience is that sweets, chocolate, ice cream and other treats can be included in a healthy diet that still allows you to keep your blood glucose under control. For instance, when I went on holiday to Cornwall at Easter, I was able to have an ice cream in Padstow because I was about to cycle back along the Camel Trail. And, at my friend's birthday party, I was allowed a slice of birthday cake because I had an extra unit of insulin to deal with it. And, every so often, a cake or choc ice after dinner is not a problem at all.

Everyone knows that sweets aren't the healthiest thing ever; it would be much easier if we all craved broccoli and Brussels sprouts rather than choccies and sugar-coated E-numbers. Sweets may be a totally delicious treat, but they're full of sugar. And – for everyone, not just people with diabetes – too much sugar is bad.

So, how do you eat sweets and treats *and* avoid hypers? It's simple. Try to save sweets for after lunch or dinner, because this way the starch in your other food slows down the sugar in the sweets, and the effect on your blood glucose is much less. Also, think about the types of sweets you eat. Chewing gum and chocolate are far better for your blood sugar than sherbet or lollipops. This is because the sugar in chewing gum is released from the gum slowly (that's how it keeps its flavour) and the fat in chocolate slows down the emptying of the stomach so that the sugar gets into your system more gradually; whereas sherbet and lollipops are both virtually pure sugar, which doesn't have to be broken down or refined once inside the body, so it can get into the bloodstream straight away. Another way to enjoy sweets and chocolates is by eating them whilst you are playing sport, doing other exercise or taking part in a P.E. lesson.

So being diabetic doesn't mean you can't have sweets or desserts, but you do have to think about their effect on your blood sugar, and there are instances where eating sweets would just be out of the question (for instance if you are hyper). It can be really annoying, and as ridiculous as it sounds, it can become a kind of psychological barrier. I've experienced this myself.

A couple of months after I was diagnosed, I was starting to become used to the idea that I had a condition that would not go

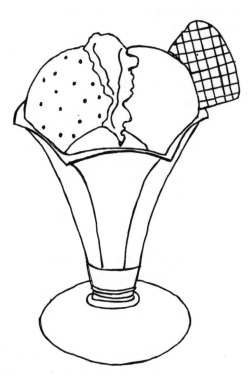

away. It was hard to get it into my head, though, that I'd have to have injections every day just to stay alive. I used to get upset almost every time I did my Lantus (glargine), then get angry with myself for being so miserable, and try to justify my anger by thinking up all the things I hated about diabetes: I had to stick needles in myself every mealtime, which hurt; I was always going hypo or hyper and it made me feel ill; I was constantly having to worry about my blood sugar and I could never just go and help myself to sweets or chocolate.

I told Mom about the way that I felt so angry a lot of the time. "Think about it," she said, "What are you actually missing out on? Is there actually anything you used to do that you can't do any more?"

There was only one thing I could think of: I couldn't just have sweets whenever I felt like it. I picked up on this and felt really annoyed about it. It may seem like a really sad thing if you've never experienced this yourself, but I became practically obsessed with chocolate.

Dad tried to rationalise it by pointing out that I wouldn't be *allowed* to just go and help myself to sweets whenever I wanted to anyway. It didn't make a bit of difference, though. The thing is, I wouldn't be *allowed*, but I *could* have. Now not only would I get in to trouble for gorging on sweets, but it would actually make me ill. And there was no point in arguing that I'd still feel sick after eating loads of chocolate anyway – I may have felt sick but I wouldn't have actually been medically ill. Now I would be.

I decided that this was the thing that diabetes actually stopped me from doing and quickly became fixated on sweets and chocolate; I used to feel depressed if I missed a P.E. lesson and therefore couldn't have my chocolate exercise snack, and I used to get what I can only call cravings for sweets. Chocolate, chewing gum, mints, ice cream, even dextrose tablets; as long as I had something sugary to eat I'd be okay. But when I couldn't have anything sweet I'd get annoyed or upset, and feel like I simply had to have *something*. I turned to sugar-free gum. I bought massive multipacks of the stuff with my pocket money and often had three or four packs on the go at one time. At my worst point, I was chomping through four pieces of gum daily – and that was on a good day.

The gum worked well, but although I always tried to make sure I was stocked up, I sometimes ran out. I usually managed okay for the day or so until I could go to the shops and buy some more, but sometimes I ended up sneaking an extra exercise snack in P.E., or serving myself slightly more ice cream with dinner than I was supposed to have.

And gum didn't stop me wanting sweets forever.

Once, I had had a really boring day at school and got home feeling really fed up. I wanted some chocolate – but I knew that I wasn't supposed to have any between meals. I wanted it anyway, so I tiptoed into the kitchen and took a bag of mini chocolate eggs, rummaged around the bag to find one that had broken in half so that I could just have part of it and not go hyper; then I ate it.

I wanted more. I tipped a few chocolate eggs out into my hand and ate them all in one go. Then, still craving more, I took another few and tried to keep them in my mouth and savour the chocolate. A minute or so later, they'd melted and dissolved. But I still wanted more.

I knew that my brother would be able to tell I'd had some of his sweets if I took any more, so instead I took the packet of dextrose from my blazer pocket and ate a couple of the tablets. I suddenly realised I was going to go really hyper if I didn't have any extra insulin.

So I found my insulin and injected another half unit. But while I was holding the needle in my stomach I remembered that too much insulin would make me go low, too – and I had no idea how much insulin I needed for what I'd just had because I couldn't remember how much I'd eaten. I pulled the needle out of my stomach before I'd counted ten seconds. Now I had no idea how much insulin had actually got into me either. I got really upset and into a real panic.

Then Mom and my brother came into the kitchen and I burst

out in tears and told my Mom what I'd just done. I knew all along it wasn't really sensible, but all that had mattered at the time had been that I wanted the chocolate.

Half an hour or so later, my blood sugar went up a bit to about 13 mmol/l, but it came down quickly, dropping to 4 mmol/l about another hour on, because of the insulin peaking. I had a snack at this point and then my blood sugar stayed okay for the rest of the day.

After this experience, I started to think that perhaps I had a mental problem or was developing a literal addiction to sugar. I felt really bad about myself and thought I seriously could be going mad. Now I know I wasn't going mad – I'm sure other people are like this when they feel like they're not allowed sweets any more...

Unfortunately, there's no substitute for willpower. The thing that made me stop chewing so much gum was when I was sorting out my bag ready to go on holiday and found that I had (I'm not joking) about six packs of gum on the go. In the cupboard I found a brand new pack that I'd just bought, and I realised just how much I was getting through. I'd also spent most of my pocket money for the last few weeks on chewing gum. I decided it was getting ridiculous and made a pact with myself that I would take one pack, and one pack only, on holiday. I wouldn't buy any more while I was away, and if I still had some left by the last day, I could keep the rest that I'd left at home. If I didn't manage it, I thought, it could possibly mean that I was actually addicted to chewing gum, in which case I would throw away every last piece of gum in the house and never buy any again. I would have to stop the habit.

I did actually manage it. However, when I got back, I'd pretty much stopped feeling like I had to have gum or sweets. I finished off what I had left – but this time it lasted much longer. Since then, I have continued to buy gum, but only occasionally – and because I want to, not because I feel I need it.

If you crave sweets...

- It's important to remember that you *can* still eat sweets. And if you eat only a reasonable amount with meals or exercise, they will cause you no problems.

- If you're a chocoholic or have a serious sweet tooth, try sugar-free gum instead of your usual sugary stuff.

- When you're out with your friends, you might find it less tempting to eat sweets if you keep a pack of sugar-free gum in your pocket. You can offer it to your friends, too, so you're not the only one having gum rather than sugary stuff.

- Bubblegum containing sugar is better than sweets that are swallowed, too, as one piece will not affect your blood sugar nearly so much as a pack of chewy sweets or a tube of sherbet. It also has the advantage that it lasts for longer – a piece of bubblegum can be chewed for an hour or so until it loses its flavour, but a chewy sweet of the same size and weight satisfies your sweet tooth for only a minute or so, and then you want another one.

- Be aware, though, that most brands of sugar-free gum can cause laxative effects if you get through loads and loads of it, so if you find yourself getting through half a pack every day, try to cut down a bit.

13
First impressions

Until I'd been diagnosed as diabetic myself – and I feel guilty to admit it now - I'd always had this perception that every diabetic person was either elderly, or overweight. With hindsight, I realise how wrong I was to think this; but, as the media is the main source of information about diabetes, unless you are personally affected by it, it follows that this is probably the perception that many people have. I think that articles and news stories related to diabetes being linked to obesity are mostly to blame. And I don't know about anyone else, but I take offence at *The Simpsons* character 'DiaBetty'. An obese woman stuffing herself sick should not be the face of diabetes. A diabetic person is a normal person trying to get on with their normal life, not a couch potato obsessed with food. I might add as well that I saw the episode featuring 'DiaBetty' a couple of years *before* I was diagnosed and haven't seen it again since, and it has still stuck in my head as being hurtful to people who are overweight, if nothing else.

I now know that these articles/news stories/characters refer *only* to type 2 diabetes, which in children is often related to weight problems; but I feel that stories of this kind don't specify enough that they apply only to *type 2* diabetes - and even if they did specify type 2 diabetes, *not everyone with type 2 diabetes is overweight*. Okay, weight problems can increase the risk of getting type 2, but would it really kill the producers of *The Simpsons* to cut out

DiaBetty's short appearances for the sake of a cheap laugh?

As a person with diabetes, I'm incredibly conscious that people who don't know about diabetes think that I have brought it on myself by getting overweight or not eating healthily. Of course, this isn't the case.

Nobody is completely certain what causes type 1 diabetes, but what is known is that some people are born with a genetic predisposition to it that is thought to be triggered later on by a virus, stressful life event or another environmental factor which isn't yet fully understood. Also, the reason that the insulin-producing beta cells in the pancreas stop working is that the immune system mistakes the cells for harmful foreign cells and kills them off. This is called an 'auto immune' problem. The lifestyle you lead is believed to make very little difference to this occurring, although it is still not fully understood by scientists. There continues to be a lot of ongoing research into the causes of type 1 diabetes.

Shortly after I was diagnosed, I was looking at the Diabetes UK website for information to try to help me understand my diabetes a bit better. Although most of what I saw was helpful, the page explaining the treatment of diabetes said "Type 1 diabetes is treated by insulin injections and diet, and regular exercise is recommended". I thought this was very misleading, as it implied that people with diabetes had to go on a diet – i.e. to lose weight. I would have been mortified if anyone read that and thought that having diabetes meant I had weight problems and needed to diet. As I felt really strongly about it, I emailed Diabetes UK and explained that I felt this information was misleading and suggested that it could be changed to make the meaning clearer. The response I received was a very positive one – their Care Advisor understood the point I was making and agreed that the phrasing was misleading, and assured me that it would be changed from "Type 1 diabetes is treated by insulin injections and diet, and regular exercise is recommended" to "Type 1 diabetes is treated by insulin injections and a healthy diet, and regular exercise is recommended". When I next looked on the

Diabetes UK website, I was pleased to see that it had indeed been changed. Only two words had been added, but to me they made a big difference.

Try to remember...

- Most people will not fully understand what diabetes is. Prejudices against people with diabetes almost always stem from ignorance.

- The best way to get people to understand diabetes is to inform them yourself. Before you were diagnosed, you may not have understood what diabetes is… and neither will other people unless someone like you can explain it to them. So, if ever someone says something to you which shows they don't understand diabetes, especially if you find what they say offensive or insulting, don't be afraid to correct them.

- Just because journalists and people in the media are more prominent in society than, say, your classmates, doesn't mean everything they say is correct or cannot be challenged. If you see diabetes-related information in the media that is incorrect or misleading and offends you, there's nothing to say you shouldn't write to the appropriate person and complain about it. You never know, they may take notice of what you say and make changes.

- If you do decide to ask for something in the media to be corrected, make sure you write to the relevant person or organisation. Do your research first, and back up what you are saying with facts or your own experience. Don't just moan; say why you feel their message should be changed

– and remember, it sounds obvious, but you are much more likely to be taken notice of if you are a) polite and b) suggest reasonable changes. For instance, don't demand that a whole web page or textbook be re-written – instead suggest, for example, that the phrase "people with diabetes should not eat sugar" could be re-worded to "people with diabetes should avoid eating lots of sugar at one time" or that "diabetes is caused by weight problems" be changed to "type 2 diabetes is sometimes caused by weight problems".

• Finally, remember that nobody will know they are mistaken until they are told so, and nobody is in a better position to educate them about diabetes than you, the person who has to live with it. So, if you know that what someone is saying is wrong, correct them. You have nothing to lose, and everyone involved – you, them, and other people with diabetes – will most definitely thank you for it in the long run.

14
Eating out

I have eaten out a number of times since I was diagnosed with diabetes. It is still possible to keep your blood sugars normal when you eat out, just as it is when you are at home. I have found that many chains of restaurants, cafes, carveries and fast-food shops will give you the nutritional values of food on their website menus, so you can calculate how much carbohydrate is in the meal that you choose.

Here are a few:
- Subway (www.subway.co.uk)
- Pizza Hut (www.pizzahut.co.uk)
- Harvester (www.harvester.co.uk)
- Toby Carveries (www.toby-carvery.co.uk)
- McDonald's (www.mcdonalds.co.uk)
- Burger King (www.burgerking.co.uk)
- Costa coffee (www.costa.co.uk)

If this sounds completely new, don't worry - this only applies if you have started carbohydrate counting to adjust your insulin doses (if you are on an insulin regime where you have two injections a day then you may not have to carb count at all). If you have not started carb counting yet, it may still be useful to look at the carbohydrate content of the meals on the menu; and if you have a set meal - for example, spaghetti bolognaise or fish and chips - that you regularly have, and that usually works out okay, i.e. you don't go hyper or hypo afterwards, then it might be helpful to work out how many grams of carbohydrate that meal contains and compare the two. Most foods have the carbohydrate content per 100 g or per product on the packet. Alternatively, there are many books on carbohydrate counting, but I wouldn't advise buying one of these until you are starting to carb count for every meal. Your diabetes nurse or dietician will explain carbohydrate counting to you when you are ready to start adjusting your insulin doses, and they will probably recommend the books that they think are best for you.

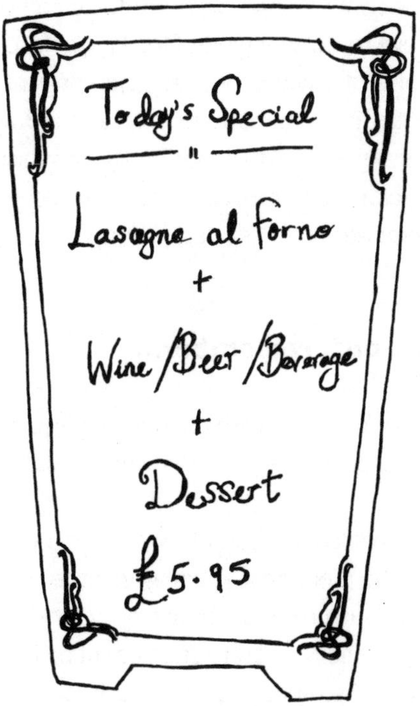

Today's Special
——— " ———

Lasagne al forno

+

Wine /Beer /Beverage

+

Dessert

£5.95

If you can work out how much carbohydrate is in one or two meals that you have at home, and you know which restaurant you are going to in advance, look on the restaurant's website beforehand to see if they provide nutritional values for their menu. If they do, I would suggest that you might print these out, or jot down the carb content of a few meals you might want to choose and take them with you when you eat out. If possible, it's best to stay on the safe side to begin with and stick to meals with similar carbohydrate contents to the meals that you would eat at home.

But once you have started carbohydrate counting, don't be afraid to experiment. The idea of a multiple-injection regime is that you have more freedom. If you are on a different insulin regime then you should discuss with your diabetes nurse how much freedom you have to change what you have for a meal. There is nothing that your diabetes should stop you from doing completely – it just means you will have to do a little bit of thinking before you try things out for the first time. If it works out well, then brilliant. But if not, try to work out why things might have gone wrong and what you could do differently next time. Don't be put off by one mistake – no one can control their blood sugar levels perfectly straight away and you will learn from experience to get better at it.

When you eat out, remember...

- If you haven't started carb counting, stick to meals similar to what you would have at home when possible.

- If you are carb counting, try to work out the carb content of meals on the menu that you may want to have. (Depending on which insulin regime you are on, your diabetes nurse or dietician may advise you to start counting the carbohydrate in your meals so that you can adjust your insulin doses accordingly and have better control of your sugar levels. It also means you can have more flexibility with the timings of your meals and allows you to eat to appetite at meal-times rather than restricting your carbohydrate consumption. Carb counting means calculating the total amount of carbohydrate in your meals and applying this to a ratio (x grams of carbohydrate to y units of insulin) to work out the dose that you need for that particular meal. If you are on a multiple-injection regime, your diabetes nurse or dietician will probably introduce you to this after a few months; however, this will depend on how quickly you get to grips with the basics of insulin treatment. Carb counting takes a little practice to begin with, but it does soon become second nature when you are doing it every day.)

• If you are carb counting, know how many grams of carbohydrate are in your meal and make sure you adjust your insulin doses accordingly. If you are having two or three courses, you can inject between courses, accounting for the carbohydrate in both. Another way to deal with this is to have two separate injections – one for the carbohydrate in the main meal and a second after dessert to account for the carbohydrate in that. The second way works well for me, but it is best to discuss this with your diabetes nurse the first time you eat out to make sure that you do what works best for you.

• If you are on a twice-daily insulin regime then you should talk to your diabetes nurse before you eat out to start with.

• Whether you are carb counting or not, try not to have high-fat meals too often – high fat content in a meal means the carbohydrate from the meal getting into your blood-stream may peak after your insulin peaks, resulting in a low blood sugar just after the meal followed by a hyper once the sugar from the meal gets into the blood. However, there's no need to avoid fatty foods completely – everything in moderation is the key.

• Also, if you are on a multiple-injection regime and you have a particularly high-fat meal, you can wait for 15 minutes or so after the meal to try and make the peak of the insulin as closely matched to the peak of the sugar as possible. This means that, because fat slows down the process of getting glucose into the blood, there will not be more insulin than necessary just after the meal when there is no extra sugar in the blood, and neither will there be sugar left over after all the insulin has acted so you will not go as high.

• Lastly, don't be surprised if your blood sugar is higher than it should be or if you have hyper symptoms just after eating a large meal. If you have injected the right amount of insulin, your blood sugar will come down to normal and your hyper symptoms will disappear very soon. Just remember, if this happens, to drink plenty of water to help it come down as quickly as possible. Good luck!

15
Parties and sleepovers

Exactly one month after I was discharged from hospital was my friend's birthday. She had a house party on her birthday, then at the weekend she invited me and my other friends to go tobogganing at the Snowdome and then for a sleepover afterwards. I was still able to go to both parties, because I was careful to take my blood sugar readings and eat my snacks when it was necessary. Your diabetes shouldn't stop you doing anything you would have done before; it just means you will have to plan a bit more.

Whenever you go out, remember your glucose meter, dextrose, Glucogel, insulin(s) and plenty of snacks. (Glucogel is a sugary gel which can be rubbed into your gums to treat a hypo if your blood sugar level is so low that you find it difficult to swallow.) Ensure your glucose meter is well stocked up with lancets and test strips; if possible take a box of ketone strips too to be on the safe side. (Ketone strips test for blood ketones if your blood sugar level is very high; because you may find it harder to control your blood sugar levels at a party or sleepover, you may be more likely to go hyper. If your sugar levels are very high *and* you have ketones, you will need to do something about it – see chapter on Illness.)

If you're going to a friend's house – whether it be for a house party, a sleepover or just for tea – ask your mom or dad to have a quick word with one of your friend's parents, just so that they're aware that you have diabetes and understand you'll have to do your blood tests and injections. If you need any help doing blood tests or injections or remembering to have snacks, make sure your friend's parents understand what they need to help you with. But if you're perfectly capable of looking after your blood sugar yourself then make sure your parent explains this. Also, if you have a mobile phone then be sure to take it with you and keep it switched on so you can contact your parents should you have any major problems (imagine the scenario where you've forgotten your meter or don't have any lancets/test strips). If you don't have a mobile, make sure you know how you can get hold of one of your parents should you need them. It's a good idea to give your home phone number to your friend's mom or dad so that they can contact your parents should you be unable to.

If you're going to a party, make sure you know beforehand what the arrangements regarding food are. If you're not sure whether you'll be able to get dinner there, have a sandwich or something light before you go, just in case, but still take your insulin so you're free to have something else to eat later. If you're going to be eating there, don't forget your insulin and remember to take spare needles. If there's going to be a birthday cake, you can still have a slice, as most shop-bought cakes will have the carbohydrate content for a fraction of the whole cake, e.g. per ¼ or per ¹/₈. Just to give you a very rough idea, a typical slice of a traditional sponge cake with icing contains about 50 grams of carbohydrate – but this varies with the size of the slice, the type of cake, thickness of the icing, decoration (marzipan, glace cherries, sugar strands) and so on.

At a sleepover you will probably stay up much later than normal, so you will often need more snacks in the late evening. Also, although you should normally try to avoid doing more than six or seven blood tests each day, when you do something outside of your normal routine (e.g. staying up later than usual, eating at different times or doing more exercise, and also if you are unwell) it is an exception to the rule; in these situations where your blood sugar levels are more difficult to control, it is more important to stop yourself from going high or hypo than to reduce the number of times you prick your fingers. At a sleepover, a safe bet is to test your blood sugar every 1 to 1½ hours after the time when you would usually go to bed; if your blood sugar is high you will usually not need anything at that point, but if it is slightly more towards the lower side then a snack is usually a good idea. As a guideline, a blood sugar of about 7 mmol/l is good before bedtime. If your blood glucose is higher than 10 mmol/l, still have a snack but make it a low G.I. one – crisps, granary toast or a mug of milk or cocoa are good. If your blood glucose is lower, it may be a good idea to have a small snack, wait 20 minutes or so and then test again – if it is the same or higher then have your normal snack and go to sleep then, but if it is still falling you should stay awake until it is steady to avoid a night-time hypo. Before you go to bed, put your dextrose, Glucogel and meter somewhere nearby and easily visible. Make sure all of your friends at the sleepover know where these are so they can get them and help you if you wake up hypo in the night.

At a house party/disco...

- When you go to a party, remember to take your glucose meter, insulin(s), snacks, dextrose tablets, Glucogel and carb counting booklet. Also take a few ketone strips – and don't forget the calibration strip for them – if at all possible. (Every time you start a new box of test strips, the meter will need to be reset by using the calibration strip in the box).

- Remember to have your regular snacks and test your blood glucose at the appropriate times.

- Dancing counts as exercise – make sure you have a small exercise snack before you hit the dance floor or you may go hypo.

- Remember as well that most drinks which are sweet - fizzy drinks especially - will contain sugar, unless they are specifically labelled "no added sugar" or "sugar free". So, with regards to drinks, you should either inject for them as you would for extra carbohydrate in food or avoid sugary drinks altogether and have a drink with no added sugar instead.

- Make sure that a few people at the party know about your diabetes and would be able to help you if you had a hypo.

- If you have a mobile phone you should take it with you and, if possible, make sure your friend's parents have your home phone number to contact your parents if necessary.

At a sleepover...

- When you go to a sleepover, take your glucose meter, insulin(s), dextrose, Glucogel and *lots* of snacks. (On my first sleepover after I was diagnosed, my Mom insisted that I take a whole carrier bag full of food, but I came back having eaten only one biscuit and a packet of crisps. The moral of the story? It doesn't matter how much food you bring back home as long as you don't run out.)

- Remember to have your regular snacks (try 10-15 carbs per extra hour you are awake, not including your bedtime snack) and test your blood glucose at the appropriate times.

- If your blood sugar is high before you go to bed, you should still have some form of a snack but make it a low G.I. one: for instance, brown or granary bread toast, a pack of crisps, a glass of milk or a mug of hot chocolate (with non-sugar sweeteners, such as saccharine).

- If your blood sugar is between 6 and 10 mmol/l, have a bedtime snack as normal. If you are verging on the low side (about 4 mmol/l), have a small amount extra to eat (this should be about 5-10 grams extra carbohydrate, e.g. a plain biscuit or two cream crackers).

- If you are hypo, treat it immediately and do not forget to have your usual bedtime snack before you go to sleep.

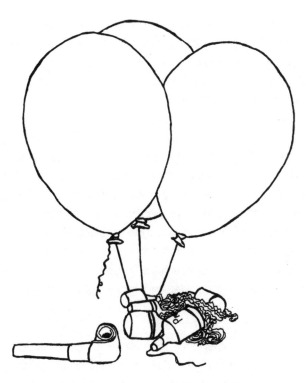

16
Daytrips

I have been on a variety of days out since I was diagnosed with diabetes: many simple shopping trips as well as trips to a theme park, a museum, the Snowdome, a cycle trail, an adventure park and an old citadel (plus one excursion to a French fort which didn't go so well, but that's a different story…).

When you go on a more active day out – and by active I mean anything sporty like swimming, cycling, football or dancing, and even just walking around (shopping counts) – take a few more of everything than you usually would. Just to give you an idea: I would allow two or three needles per injection you will need to do, four lancets and three test strips per hour you plan to be out, two or three packets of dextrose, one tube of Glucogel, two or three small chocolate bars or similar and one starchy snack per hour you'll be out (though don't feel you have to use all this). And don't forget your carb counting booklet and mobile phone if you have them. Bear in mind as well that you'll need a starchy snack afterwards if you go hypo.

From my experience, surprisingly, it can be harder to control your blood sugar during a day or several hours of less energetic exercise than during an hour or two of flat-out sport. I have usually coped well with running, swimming, netball and athletics but during and after days out shopping I have often had a hypo followed a few hours later by a high reading, or the other way around. Walking around shops, to a friend's house or between rides at a theme park may not seem very energetic, but can actually have far more of an effect on your blood sugar than you might imagine.

I mentioned earlier about the time when we went to an old fort whilst on holiday in France. I'd eaten a few squares of chocolate as an exercise snack as soon as we got out of the car outside Ville-franche, an old village near the villa where we were staying. It was right at the foot of the mountains; from the car park we could see a stone building half way up the nearest peak. We started walking around the village. There were a few interesting souvenir shops and some old caves, but there wasn't a lot to do there so we started walking back.

Then we saw a tall archway which looked like the entrance to something. We went over and a man was there selling tickets to get into the fort on the mountainside. Without really thinking about my blood sugar, we handed over some money and started walking up the steps to the fort. It wouldn't have been so bad if the steps had been out in the open air, but instead we were in a narrow, poorly-lit tunnel going through the mountain itself. The steps were steep, but we went up them quite quickly.

When, after a few minutes, we got to the top of the first section of stairs, there was an alcove with a small window to let in some natural light and fresh air. We stepped into the alcove so that I could have another exercise snack before carrying on.

But before I could get my dextrose out of my pocket, I started to feel slightly dizzy. A split second later, I experienced a sickening jolt inside my head, like someone had punched my forehead really hard. I felt faint and nauseous, and white dots began to appear in front of my eyes. It was like something was crushing and rattling my brain inside my skull, and whilst my cheeks were burning as though I had red hot irons pressed to my face, my arms felt like they were trapped in ice, and I was shivering.

Then I was sick. Three times. My vision went back to normal, but I was still dizzy and faint. It was so claustrophobic – I felt like I just had to get out of there. But the only two ways out were up the steps to the fort or down the steps to the village. I couldn't risk carrying on up the steps – what if it happened again? – and I was too scared to step out of the alcove and start off down the steps because I was so dizzy and could easily fall down them to my certain death.

As soon as I started to feel better, I sat on the top step next to my mom, clinging to the handrail. I took my blood sugar, expecting it to be about 2 mmol/l, but it was actually 6.7 mmol/l. We guessed that what had probably happened was that, not having had any dextrose before going up all those steps, I had gone badly hypo – but my pancreas had released glucagon, which made my blood sugar come back up, which was why I was now fine. Well, not completely fine, but a lot better than I had been.

We decided that Dad and my younger brother Robert would carry on up to the fort, but Mom and I would gradually make our way down the stairs and wait for them outside the entrance. I shuffled down a few steps at a time, still shaky and scared to stand up. In the meantime, I ate a packet of crisps (very slowly to make sure it wouldn't make me sick) to keep my blood sugar up.

I now understand why I had this horrible experience: I should have had some dextrose before we started walking up the steps. I suppose it was just something we wouldn't normally have had to think about – sometimes you don't realise how something will affect you until you come to do it. It can be hard to know how to keep your blood sugar at the right level when you try something new, so below are some suggestions from my own experience.

Shopping

If you're out shopping for a few hours, you'll be on your feet walking around most of the time, so an extra snack or two may be needed. Make sure you have any snacks you would usually have before you start walking around; about one hour afterwards, take a blood sugar reading. If it is an hour or longer before your next meal is due, then, obviously as long as you are not hyper, it might be worthwhile having another snack at this point. Some good snacks at this time could be a biscuit, a handful of raisins or a small chocolate bar; as the exercise for the next hour or so will be spread out, dextrose or sugar-based exercise snacks will peak before the sugar is needed in the blood. On the other hand, very starchy foods will peak about two hours later, probably causing a blood sugar level slightly higher than the usual range just as you are about to eat your next meal, and possibly causing a hypo or hypo symptoms during the time beforehand as the extra sugar will not yet have got into the bloodstream when the sugar already in the blood is being used up.

Theme parks

As a daytrip to a theme park usually involves some walking around (which will in turn mean the need for more regular snacks), it's probably a good starting point to begin as you would if you were going shopping (see above). Remember to test your blood sugar whenever you feel it necessary. I would advise doing a test at least every two hours the very first time you go on a trip like this – this will be a good way of making sure you are getting the timing of snacks right. Fall behind with snacks and you will go hypo; overdo it and you will go high. Experimenting with different exercise snacks will help you to understand – and ultimately, take control of – your blood sugar levels and the way they are affected by different types of exercise and snacks.

Having said this, it's important to be sensible, stay on the safe side if you're unsure, and test your blood sugar regularly after any changes to what you would normally do. And be sure to talk through the plans for the day with your parents and/or diabetes nurse before you go, and ask any questions or queries you have about what you're supposed to do and when.

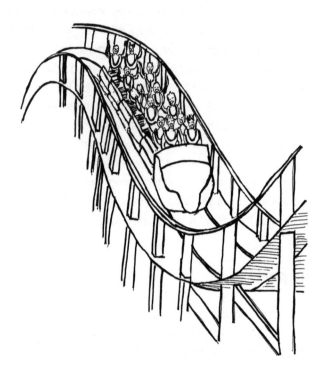

If you go on a ride that you know will scare you, take a blood sugar reading within 10 minutes before taking a seat on it, and then again as soon as possible after you come off. Being scared affects different people in different ways at different times; it could bring your blood sugar level up *or* down. If you think there is any chance of your having a hypo whilst you are on the ride, take a dextrose tablet just before you go on it to be on the safe side.

If you are hyper before you join the queue for a scary ride, it's definitely best to wait until your blood sugar has come down to normal first – stress increases the need for insulin, which means it is possible that getting stressed out on a scary ride will push your blood sugar up even more. Even if you think you might not still have the guts to go on it in half an hour's time, it's surely better not to go on it at all than to go on and deeply regret it. You have to admit that the last thing you want is to develop blurry eyes and a headache whilst upside down, travelling at a speed of 100 mph through mid-air, awaiting a 50 metre freefall, or any combination of the above.

And ensure that hypos are properly treated before you go on any ride, to avoid a similar situation. If the ride has a long queue, it can be difficult to know what to do, because you may take a blood sugar reading before joining the queue and yet it can have changed dramatically by the time you are seated on the ride.

For obvious reasons, it's not possible to take a rucksack or handbag onto most thrill rides, but from my experience the opera-tors at theme parks will usually look after important belongings such as glucose meters while you are on the ride. If this is the case, take your glucose meter into the queue with you and leave your other belongings with someone who isn't going on it. Take a reading sev-eral minutes before it is your turn and take one or two dextrose tablets if you are in the fours (4+ mmol/l) or think it will fall in the next 15 minutes, then hand your meter over to the ride operator as you are about to get onto the ride. Always keep your dextrose with you – if you experience any hypo symptoms when you are un-able to take a blood sugar reading then take two or three dextrose tablets to be on the safe side and test as soon as possible.

From my experience, a packet of dextrose tablets will not fall out of a jeans pocket on an upside down rollercoaster (not that I intend to go on that one again!). Similarly, if you have a big enough pocket there is nothing to stop you from taking your meter on with you – but make sure it is secure, as a lost glucose meter will cause a lot of problems. If in any doubt, don't risk it.

On less scary rides (I'm thinking pirate ships, spinning teacups, right-way-up rollercoasters) you should be able to take a handbag or rucksack with you. Put it on the floor in front of you and put one foot through the handles to stop it from falling out of the side.

Finally – and I'm sure you don't need me to point this out – it's very rarely possible to take a blood sugar reading whilst on a ride. If you think you are going hypo whilst you are on a ride, take two or three dextrose tablets if possible and check your blood sugar as soon as you come off.

If you think you might be hypo whilst you are sitting on the ride waiting for it to start, you *must* shout to the operator to wait until you have done your blood test. If they take no notice to start with, persist. It'll be no fun for you if you're stuck in your seat feeling ill, not knowing if you're going low. If it turns out you are hypo, *get off*, you can always queue again, but if you go on when you are hypo you might end up feeling very ill whilst you are on it – not a good situation to be in. If your blood glucose is normal, tell the operator that you are okay and the ride can start again.

On an active day out...

- When you go on a day trip, especially without your parents, it's very important that you have everything with you. As always, this means your glucose meter, insulin(s), dextrose, Glucogel and a couple more snacks than you think you'll need.

- If you're going with your mates, make sure that at least two or three of them know about your diabetes. Tell them which pocket or where in your bag you've put your dextrose, meter and Glucogel and make sure they know, and would be able to recognise, the symptoms of hypers and especially hypos. (Hyper symptoms are: blurred vision, headache, extreme thirst, breath smelling of acetone (like pear drops). Hypo symptoms are: shaking, going pale, feeling sick, dizzy or lightheaded, disturbed vision, extreme hunger, tiredness, confusion).

- You should also carry some form of identification to show that you have diabetes. This may make you feel "different" or the odd one out – nobody really wants to feel tagged by a medical condition they can't help having. However, carrying ID doesn't mean wearing a hat with a great big neon sign saying "I've got diabetes". You can get diabetes ID cards which you can put in your pocket, purse or wallet, wristbands which medics would recognise to mean you have diabetes or even special necklaces and bracelets which look like normal jewellery but with your condition engraved into the back of it. Most people wouldn't be able to tell that you have diabetes at a glance from any of these.

• Remember to have your regular snacks and test your blood glucose at the appropriate times.

• On a day out taking part in more energetic sports like football, swimming or cycling, you'll need regular exercise snacks. Remember to check your blood glucose first – it should be at least 6 mmol/l before you start exercising.

• Also check your blood sugar when you finish exercising, to make sure you have had the correct exercise snacks, and be sure to have a bedtime snack that day to prevent night-time hypos.

17
The honeymoon phase

I'm sure your diabetes nurse will have explained this to you already, but basically, when you are first diagnosed, most of the beta cells in your pancreas have stopped producing insulin; the ones which are left are working overtime to get as much insulin into the body as possible, but this still isn't enough, which is why you need to inject extra insulin. When you start having injections, the few beta cells that are still working take a break – with enough insulin getting into the bloodstream now, they do not need to make any more. After a while, the beta cells go back to work. As they are now producing insulin again, the amount of extra insulin that is needed decreases, so your insulin doses can go down. This is the honeymoon phase (note that not everyone has a honeymoon phase). During my honeymoon phase, my carbohydrate to Novorapid (aspart) insulin ratio went from 10 grams:1 Unit to 30 grams:1 Unit and my Lantus (glargine) dose fell from 10 Units to 6 Units. (In other words, I needed only a third of the rapid-acting insulin I had when I came out of hospital, and less long-acting insulin too).

After several months of the honeymoon phase, the beta cells get worn out and stop making insulin altogether. The honeymoon phase is then over (for most people, it lasts for something between three months and a year).

I started to come out of the honeymoon phase literally over-night. My blood sugar levels had been very good for the past few weeks – I had rarely gone hyper and couldn't remember off the top of my head when I had last had a hypo. Then suddenly I woke up one morning with a reading of 12.5 mmol/l – the highest it had ever been before breakfast.

I added on a correction dose of 1 Unit to my breakfast Novorapid (aspart), which would usually have brought my blood sugar down by 4 mmol/l, but it stayed about the same. It went on like this for the rest of the day, and, although I was at 9 mmol/l before breakfast the next morning, it went up to 21 mmol/l within 1½ hours. I knew that something was changing and that I needed more insulin.

At lunchtime, we worked my Novorapid (aspart) out on a ratio of 1 Unit:20 grams. I still went high afterwards, so Mom phoned my diabetes nurse, who said that either I was coming down with a sore throat or something or I was coming out of the honeymoon phase. Over the next two days, I gradually adjusted my insulin to carbohydrate dose down to 1Unit:10 grams. This is about average for people who are not in the honeymoon phase.

At first, I felt like I was giving myself much too much insulin; a meal which usually would have needed 3 Units now needed 9. I knew that these were normal doses, but I also knew that if I had injected 9 Units just one week earlier I would have gone dangerously hypo.

A few weeks after this, my carbohydrate to Novorapid (aspart) insulin ratio actually settled at 15 grams:1 Unit.

However, (this is where it gets a little bit confusing!) after speaking to my diabetes nurse at the diabetes clinic following this adjustment, we came to the conclusion that I'm not actually completely out of the honeymoon phase yet, as I am still taking relatively small doses for my age and weight.

The honeymoon phase is different for different people. For some people it will start and end gradually, for others it will mean more sudden changes. And of course, there are many people who don't have a honeymoon phase of any description at all. It varies from person to person. Basically, if you have just been diagnosed then watch out for hypos as they may indicate your insulin doses need lowering – and once you are in the honeymoon phase, look out for any recurring high readings, which could show that your honeymoon phase is coming to an end.

Going into the honeymoon phase...

- Remember that your insulin doses are likely to fall by quite a lot within the first month or so that you are on insulin.

- If you are often going hypo then you will have to lower your doses, but discuss this with your diabetes nurse first.

- Try not to make too many changes all at once – if you change every dose and every snack you have in just one day then it will be virtually impossible to find out what's working and what isn't.

- Talk to your diabetes nurse before you make any major changes, but try to have in mind what you think you should do before you ask for advice. This will help you to understand not just *what* you are changing, but *why*.

Coming out of the honeymoon phase...

- You will definitely notice changes in your blood sugar levels when you are coming out of the honeymoon phase...

- ...but high readings for a day or two do not necessarily mean this is happening. A cold or infection could have the same effect on your readings, which is why it is important not to increase your doses too quickly; if you treble the amount of insulin you are having when your immune system is actually starting to get rid of a cold, you will end up with lots of hypos.

• Increase your doses gradually. If you are using rapid-acting insulin with every meal then try to stick to medium Glycaemic Index meals whilst you are finding the right carbohydrate to insulin ratio, so that your blood sugar peaks when your insulin does and you don't have any misleading readings.

• Test your blood glucose regularly: it is especially important when you are finding the right insulin doses. If you are using rapid-acting insulin then you should test about two and a quarter hours after you do your injection. If it is within 3 mmol/l of what it was before your meal then you have the right dose. If it is much higher you need to increase the dose, and if it is lower you need to reduce it. But still try to stick to a maximum of six or seven blood tests a day or your fingers will end up aching.

18
Blood tests

When I was told about my glucose meter in hospital, the thought of doing four blood tests every day was horrendous. Going by the first one that I had had at the doctor's surgery (the GP must have had the lancer - the device which pushes the needle into the skin - on the highest setting possible because it was really painful and I had a bruise on my thumb for two weeks), it was going to be horrible.

Doing blood tests on my own meter, though, was nowhere near as bad. I was shown that I could adjust how deep the lancet (the needle used to prick the skin) went into my finger and make it hurt a lot less. I got used to doing blood tests before every meal and soon I didn't even think twice before pressing the button on the lancer. Blood tests became as much a part of my daily routine as brushing my teeth.

In fact, I got so used to them that for a few months I used to be doing every five minutes — or it seemed like it. I really wouldn't recommend this, but there were actually several occasions where I would be sitting in a really boring lesson and decide to take a reading to try to pass the time.

I became fixated on the number 4 - the threshold of hypo. Once, when I was riding my bike, I saw on my computer that I was going at 3.9 mph and panicked, thinking that was my blood sugar level. For two or three months, I went through a phase where I was never doing less than about 10 blood tests a day — actually, it was common for me to do 16 or 17. It wasn't because I thought I needed to do them, but I wanted to keep checking my blood sugar "just in case". Gradually, though, I stopped taking so many readings as I became more confident that I was having the right insulin and snacks, but also I learnt to trust the way that I felt more.

It had also occurred to me that there might be times, if I went really hypo and got confused, when I might be unable to set the meter and lancer up for myself. It would be a good idea if my friends knew how to. So I taught all of my friends how to set the lancer up with a lancet, how to put the test strips into the meter and then how to put the blood on the end of the test strip to take a reading. I also taught them what was hypo (less than 4 mmol/l),

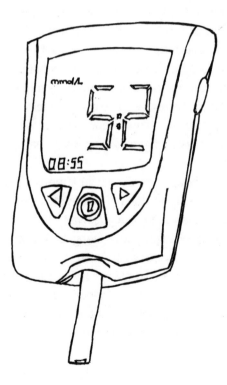

what was normal (between 4 and 10 mmol/l), and what was high (above 10 mmol/l), and what to do if I was hypo or hyper. (If you are hypo, friends need to be aware that you have to have some form of sugar (e.g. dextrose tablets or a sugary drink), sit still and wait for your blood sugar levels to come back up, and if you are out with them while you're hypo they should never leave you on your own. If they are able to, they should also help you to do your blood tests if you become confused. However, if they can't help you do a blood test, the important thing is that they know how to recognise the warning signs of a hypo and can help you treat one if you are unable to do so yourself. If you are hyper, your friends should understand that you should drink plenty of water and you must not eat. If you ever become unconscious while you are out with your friends, they should call an ambulance immediately and say that you are diabetic.) I have never needed one of my friends to do a blood test for me (yet), but I know that they would be able to if ever it was necessary. My younger brother Robert also knows what blood sugars are normal, high and low, and he knows where my meter, dextrose and Glucogel are kept in the house so he can get them if I suddenly feel ill. It's really important that your friends/siblings would know what to do if something wasn't right, so they would be able to help you if it was necessary.

Of course, though, there's not just the problem of actually doing the blood tests. If you don't want people to know about your diabetes then blood tests can be a giveaway – not that many people would recognise the gadget you're using as a glucose meter, but they will probably be curious as to what it is and are likely to ask awkward questions. You could always try dodging them by saying that it's a calculator, like one of my friends did when a girl in my P.E. class was questioning me about it! Even if they don't believe it, they should realise that it's not something you want to tell them and stop asking.

Tips for doing blood tests

- Adjust the lancer if you have problems doing the finger pricks. If it hurts very often, try setting the lancer to a lower number; if you regularly don't get enough blood then try it on a higher number.

- Don't keep squeezing your fingers to get more blood out. If you don't get enough the first time, try again on a different finger.

- Make sure there is enough blood on the test strip, otherwise you may get a false reading.

- Always double-check any readings that don't make sense. No glucose meter is 100% correct 100% of the time; there could have been a problem with the test strip, food on your hands, not enough blood on the test strip, the meter wasn't calibrated – and so on.

- If you're still at the stage where you don't want to be asked any awkward questions, you can do your blood tests with the meter on your lap under the desk in lessons, and go to the toilets to do your blood test before lunch. Don't get stressed about it, though, and don't look around to check that nobody's watching when you do a blood test. Looking so uneasy will draw attention to yourself – the exact opposite of what you want. And, although you might not think it, most of the time people won't even notice what you're doing.

19
Illness

When I was first diagnosed with diabetes, the thought of becoming ill was even more unpleasant than normal, as I'd been told that illness could affect my sugar levels drastically and even make blood ketones build up. My diabetes nurse had also told me that people with diabetes are sometimes admitted to hospital as a precaution if they have sickness and diarrhoea. As you can imagine, if you are unable to keep food down, it makes your blood sugar levels very hard to control, because you still need some insulin even if you are not eating.

At the time of writing, I've been lucky as I haven't had any significant illness since my diagnosis. Apart from the usual run of colds (none of which has affected my sugar levels), there's only been one occasion when I was off my food for a day. I felt really nauseous – although I wasn't actually sick – and completely lost my appetite. Fortunately, my blood sugar levels weren't affected much by it, and I never had any more than a trace of blood ketones. Although I couldn't eat any food, I was able to sip hot chocolate to keep my blood sugar levels stable. I had my Lantus (glargine) injection as usual, but didn't inject any Novorapid (aspart) for the drinks I was having, because each time I wasn't having more than my usual snack of 15 grams carbohydrate.

It is advisable for people who have diabetes to have the flu jab. This is because – and the same goes for anyone with a chronic condition – you are more at risk of developing complications such as pneumonia if you do catch the flu, and it can cause a lot of problems in maintaining steady blood glucose levels. Your diabetes nurse can advise you on this.

I had the flu jab for the first time in December 2008 at a flu vaccination clinic at my local doctors' surgery. It wasn't really a big deal having the jab, although I did feel a bit odd being the youngest there as practically everyone else seemed to be over 65. If you feel awkward about this, speak to your GP – as mine did, they may suggest you make an appointment with them to have the jab, rather than having it at the same time as everyone else.

Sick day rules

- Unusually high blood sugar levels can sometimes be the first sign of illness.

- Never stop taking your insulin. You should only reduce your dose because of sickness after being advised to do so by your diabetes nurse. It is important, if you are unwell, that you contact your diabetes team early.

- If you've lost your appetite, keep drinking sugary drinks like fruit juice, fizzy drinks or hot drinks with sugar, in place of your normal snacks and meals. Alternatively, you could try eating small bowls of jelly – but not a type with reduced sugar, as the point is to stop yourself from going hypo. However, you should not inject for this unless you have more carbohydrate than you would for a normal snack.

- Between meals or sugary drinks, you should have plenty of sugar-free fluids to keep hydrated.

- If you are unwell and your blood sugar level is above 14 mmol/l, you should test your blood or urine for ketones. If you have more than a trace (blood ketone level 0.6 mmol/l or higher), you should repeat the test in one to two hours. If you have ketones, you should contact your diabetes nurse as soon as possible for advice.

- If you are unwell but your blood sugar levels are normal, you should still test your blood or urine for ketones, and follow the same advice as above.

- Rest. Exercise can make ketones worse if your blood sugar level is high.

- When you are ill, if in any doubt as to what to do, always contact your diabetes team. Stick to the advice you are given and hopefully you will be able to treat your illness at home; most minor illnesses can be managed safely, and it is rare to have to be admitted to hospital.

20
Holidays

When I first came out of hospital, it was hard to imagine getting on with my day-to-day life without feeling like I was living to do my next injection. Just the thought of doing my injections at school seemed impossible, let alone spending a week miles away from home. But at the same time, I knew that at some point I was going to go on holiday again, and that, however hard it was to believe at that time, I would eventually be able to cope with going away again.

It was actually only a few months later that we booked a holiday in a cottage in Cornwall for a week in the Easter holidays. I was really looking forward to it – we'd been to Cornwall every Easter since before I could remember, so it would be nice to carry on with something I'd done before -   but I was really nervous about it too. By this point I was doing my injections without any problems, so mental images of us all sitting in a motorway café for an hour waiting for me to do my injections were not an issue; but there were other things I was worried about. How much stuff should we take? What would we do if there was a problem and I had to go to hospital? Would I still be able to go everywhere and do everything I used to? Or would it just not be the same anymore?

Luckily, I had no problems whilst we were away. We took enough of everything (in fact, possibly quite a bit *too* much), and I had no real issues with my blood sugar. I still cycled the Camel Trail, with exercise snacks every hour, and went to Crealy (Adventure

Park) as always, without any problems. The thing that surprised me the most was that nothing felt different to how it normally was when I went. I was expecting to feel a sense of disappointment as I visited all of the places which I had always loved to come to before, but I felt like everything was exactly the same.

At the start of the summer holidays, we went on a five-day adventure holiday in Devon, doing activities such as rock climbing, abseiling, canoeing and zipwire. By this point I had more experience of controlling my blood sugar and managed to do all of these activities without any hypos. I was also able, with the help of my mom and a carbs book, to take the right amount of insulin for meals of which I didn't know the exact carbohydrate content.

Then, in August, I went to Provence in the South of France for a week with my Mom, Dad, brother, Nan and Grandad. We went to the same villa as we had done the previous two years; in fact that house is probably our favourite out of all of the places we've ever been on holiday. So, while I was really looking forward to it, part of me was dreading going back to the same lovely place in case I felt somehow disappointed – after all, nothing was going to be *exactly* the same now I was having to worry about my blood sugar, was it?

Actually, I was surprised and relieved, when we got there, that I didn't feel like it was different at all. The holiday was great and the week flew by, with only one time when I felt a bit upset about things. It was in the middle of the week, after dinner; I'd just done my Lantus (glargine) injection and it had hurt a lot more than normal. Suddenly it hit me that when I had come here last year, and the year before, I hadn't had to have any injections. I hadn't spent my holidays worrying about my blood sugar levels. Holidays had been a chance to leave most of my problems at home; as soon as I'd got off the plane I'd put any worries I had on hold and just focused on enjoying the week. Now it dawned on me that it wasn't so simple to put my diabetes on hold. It just wasn't possible. It isn't. All of a sudden I felt bitter about the fact that here I was, in the same sunny villa in the same week of August – but it wasn't the same holiday as the year before. Then I'd been able to just go swimming or have an ice cream without having to count carbs or have injections or worry about what my blood sugar was doing all the time. I'd been able to have a change from the normal routine of a school week – the only timing that had really been important was getting out of the villa before 10 am on the last day. Now there was a whole new set of times to live by; not just morning, afternoon and evening, but time to have Lantus and time to check blood sugar and have snacks. With diabetes, everything had to be planned and prepared and counted.

The thing is, when you have diabetes, it's a full-time job. Unfortunately, you don't get holidays from it. And however far from home you travel, your diabetes always goes with you. It's like having an especially heavy piece of luggage to cart around on top of your normal suitcases – only you don't have the option of leaving it somewhere on the way. However, just because you can't have a holiday without diabetes, that doesn't mean you can't have a holiday at all. As always, you will need to take care of your blood sugar levels

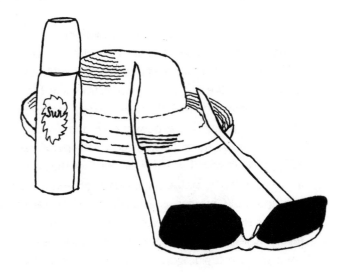

during your holiday, but that shouldn't mean you enjoy your holiday any less. Controlling your diabetes in new surroundings is really no different to at home, so there's no need to worry about it causing problems. Do as you would normally, talk to your diabetes nurse before you go and most importantly, enjoy your holiday.

Before you go on holiday...

• Talk to your diabetes nurse a few weeks before you go.

• Make sure you pack all of your supplies of insulin, needles etc the day before you go away. If you leave it until first thing in the morning before you set off, you're more than likely to forget something in the hurry.

• It's better to be safe than sorry, so if you're not sure how many of something to take, estimate higher rather than lower. The general advice is to take double of everything.

• Insulin cartridges need to be kept cool when they are not in the insulin pen, so keep cartridges out of sunlight and put them in a fridge as soon as possible. You could use an ice pack to keep the insulin cool whilst travelling, but I would really recommend FRIO™ wallets instead as they keep the insulin at a temperature between 18 and 26°c for several days. (Insulin starts to degrade at temperatures above 30°c.) I have two FRIO™ wallets – one for the insulin pens I am using and one for the spare cartridges and the glucagon injection kit. (Glucagon is a hormone which raises blood sugar levels, and in the event that a person with diabetes has a severe hypo leading to unconsciousness, they will need to have a glucagon injection. You should have been given and shown how to use a glucagon injection kit when you were first diagnosed.) You should not need to carry the spare cartridges or glucagon kit with you if you go out for the day whilst away, but make sure you keep one at your accommodation, in a FRIO™ wallet.

• If you're travelling by plane or abroad, you will need a letter from your diabetes nurse or doctor as evidence that you need to take insulin and needles onto the plane. You should make sure you have this to hand when you get to the air-port and be prepared that you may have to show the letter when you go through security. However, I've travelled by plane twice since I was diagnosed and have not been asked to show the letter; probably as the airport staff will have seen needles and lancets going through security many times before and recognise them.

• If you're going by plane you will also need to carry all of your supplies in your hand luggage. If it goes in a suitcase in the hold there is a chance it could be lost on the way – and there is no way you can afford to be without insulin. Moreover, insulin will freeze if it is put into the hold, and will become unusable.

• It's also advisable to share needles, lancets and insulin between two pieces of hand luggage. This is so that if one bag is lost or stolen, you will still have enough medical supplies for at least the first few days of your holiday, giving you the chance to find a hospital and collect some more before you run out.

• Make sure you have plenty of both starchy and sugary snacks. You should have enough snacks to keep your blood sugar from falling too low if there are any delays on the way there; and you should make sure you have several packets of dextrose tablets in your hand luggage.

21
The diabetes clinic

You were probably told when you were diagnosed that you would have an appointment at the Diabetes Clinic roughly every four months. The reason for these appointments is to look at how well you are controlling your blood sugar levels, and to provide an opportunity for you to ask any questions. It is also for your diabetes nurse, dietician and/or consultant to get a picture of how you are coping in general and to advise you on how you can improve your blood glucose control.

This is how the clinic usually works: you'll be measured, weighed and have a blood sample taken for the HBA1c test. (This is where a sample of blood is taken from your finger and sent to a lab so you can get a picture of how your glucose levels have been on average for the past few weeks. The HBA1c result will be given as a percentage, that is equivalent to the percentage of haemoglobin, a chemical in the blood, which has glucose attached to it). After this you will speak to the diabetes nurse, dietician and consultant about your insulin doses, blood sugar levels, eating habits etc and your injection sites may be checked for lumps (see page 92).

Soon after your appointment at the clinic, you should be told what the result of the HBA1c test was. The target HBA1c is usually under 7.5%.

Also, once a year you will have a more detailed check-up (starting after a few years of your having diabetes). You will have a blood test to check that your thyroid gland is working properly and to look for signs of coeliac disease, a urine test to check for kidney problems, and your eyes will be screened for signs of retinopathy (a condition where the blood vessels in the retina at the back of the eye leak and cause damage to the eye – it can be a complication of diabetes after many years of high sugar levels). Your feet will also be checked for signs of diabetes-related foot problems, such as poor circulation, diabetic neuropathy (nerve damage) and ulcers.

At the time of writing this, I haven't yet had an annual check-up so can't write about any first-hand experience of this.

The really important thing to remember is that the diabetes clinic shouldn't be something you worry about or get worked up over. You might be a bit nervous before you go to the clinic for the first time, but you really have nothing to be anxious about – the staff are there to help you, not to tell you off if things aren't going right.

Once you've gone to the clinic and are still waiting for your HBA1c results, you may feel like you're waiting for exam results. Remember it's a test for your blood sugar, not for you. If you know that you've been doing what you can to keep your blood sugar levels where they're supposed to be, then you can expect your HBA1c to reflect this. But if your results come back and your HBA1c is higher than the acceptable level of 7.5%, remember that it's not too late to do something about it so your results are better next time. If you know that you haven't been controlling your sugar levels quite as well as you could have done, whatever the reason may be, see it as a chance to improve. Even if it's not the first time your HBA1c has been too high, you can still make a difference to the long term. I try not to think about all the horrible complications, like eye damage, kidney failure, heart disease and neuropathy (nerve damage), but they are at the back of my mind. We need to know about the complications which could come as a consequence of not controlling our blood sugars; I'll be the first to admit that, if I didn't know I could end up blind or on dialysis because of neglecting my sugar levels, I probably wouldn't bother looking after them. It's hard, being young and thinking about becoming old. But some day in the future, it will happen - and making a few sensible decisions now could mean the difference between thinking about complications today and living with them in years to come.

This is why it is so important that you do try hard to keep your blood sugars as close to the target range as is possible. Not only will you end up having fewer hypos and hypers but you will also be reducing the risk of complications later on. And it is worth it when your HBA1c tests come back just as good as, or better than, expected.

If you're nervous about going to the diabetes clinic...

- Nobody likes having to go to hospitals and clinics, but re-member that it is for your benefit in the long run. If you ever start to develop complications in the future, then the diabetes clinic will be a chance to pick up on them so that they can be treated or prevented from getting worse.

- Also, it's not only long-term complications that can be caught before they get worse – while you might find it hard to spot lipodistrophy (lumps – see next chapter) yourself until they become very bad, your diabetes nurse will be able to spot these at the diabetes clinic before there are any serious problems. Then you will be able to avoid the affected area and the lumps will go much more quickly.

- And remember that there is nothing about going to the diabetes clinic that you should be worrying about. You may be nervous in case you find out that something isn't quite right, but prevention is better than cure; if you think about it, then I'm sure you would rather catch any problems now and get rid of them than leave them until they are out of control and there's nothing that can be done.

• The clinic is also a good opportunity for you to ask any questions you have about anything that involves your diabetes.

• On top of this, if it is your first clinic appointment, they won't be expecting your HBA1c to be perfect – it will include some of the high sugar levels from before you started taking the insulin. For example, my HBA1c was 13% when I was first diagnosed but by my first clinic appointment it had come down to 9%, and it had come down again to 7.3%, well within the normal range, by my second appointment. As long as it has come down from when you were first diagnosed, then you know you're off to a good start.

• Depending on your age and other factors, you may be on any of several insulin regimes. As you get older, you may be advised to change to a multiple-injection regime – although you will not be forced to change regime unless you are happy to do so. Bear in mind, though, that a multiple-injection regime allows you to have more freedom to eat what you want (within reason) and not have to stick to such a strict routine; so, if you are advised to go onto a different regime I would advise that you do at least think about it.

22

Lumps (lipodistrophy)

When you're first diagnosed with diabetes, you're taught how to do your injections and told to rotate the injection sites – then you see pictures of lipodistrophy to show you *why* you have to rotate them. The lumps develop because insulin stimulates the growth of subcutaneous (under the skin) fat layers – if you keep injecting in the same area then this effect will be more pronounced, resulting in lipodistrophy. While you can help to stop lumps from developing by being careful to rotate, they can sometimes appear even when you think you're not doing anything wrong.

It was at the diabetes clinic that I discovered that I had what was starting to be a lump in my right leg. Although I thought I'd been rotating my injection sites well, it looked like I'd developed a "favourite site" for my injections, in the middle of my right leg – something I was completely unaware of until my diabetes nurse pointed it out. I couldn't see the lump, but I could feel that there was something there.

I avoided the area around the lump like the plague for the next couple of months. I could feel that there definitely was a lump there now and it also felt like I had another one starting to appear on my other leg. I got really stressed out about it - after another few weeks I was convinced that I had only a few square inches of my legs which hadn't got any lumps. I felt like it was closing in on me – I desperately didn't want to move to a different injection site as

I felt like I'd ruined enough of me already with my needles. But at the same time I knew that I couldn't keep injecting into lumps: they would keep getting worse and become much more painful, but also the insulin would not be absorbed effectively through lumps and cause hypers.

I told the diabetes nurse about the lumps, and she came to check them – but actually, it turned out that there were no lumps there at all – even the one that had been there had gone. She explained that, whilst I had been checking for lumps sitting down, you are supposed to check for them whilst standing up. I had obviously been mistaken about the lumps getting worse, thinking that because it was sore, and because my leg felt different when I checked for lumps sitting down, there were lumps there – when the only one that had really existed had actually been getting better all along.

Lumps *will* go if you avoid them. And you can help avoid getting them in the first place by rotating your injection sites properly. Having said this, surveys show that around half of all people with diabetes will get lumps at some point, so you're not alone if you do find that you develop them. The important thing is to make sure you rotate your injection sites as much as possible and that if you do find any lumps, you should avoid injecting into them. Remember that they will go eventually.

If you think you may have lipodistrophy...

- Check for lumps in your legs or stomach when standing up, *not* sitting down. The normal fat layer in these injection sites can be pushed together when you are sitting down, resulting in what looks and feels like a small lump but actually isn't.

- If your skin looks shiny this can also indicate that there is a lump there.

- If you find that you do have a lump, make sure you avoid it completely. It will usually go within a few months as long as you leave it alone. You might think that, as the lump is just fat, losing weight will help to get rid of it. I thought this, but I asked my diabetes nurse about it and she said that dieting doesn't make any difference to lipodistrophy.

23
The last word

It's now 2009. Christmas has been and gone and a brand new year has begun. Since I was diagnosed at the start of January 2008, I've also come to the end of my first year with diabetes. It's been a crazy, emotional, unpredictable year; downright depressing at the worst of times but absolutely flipping fabulous at best. If life is a rollercoaster, this year has been the Pepsi Max.

Reading back through everything I've written, I'm starting to see that actually, I've come an amazingly long way in the last 12 months. When I was first diagnosed, diabetes seemed like a death sentence - though now, of course it's still there, but to be honest I don't really think about it. If it wasn't for my diabetes I would never have written this book – and I've wanted to be a writer since I was tiny. So really, out of all the upset that my diabetes caused, has come one of the most fantastic things I could have wished for.

I know that when you're first diagnosed it is hard. The first few weeks, the first few months, can be the scariest time you can imagine. I don't blame you if you're frightened. I don't blame you if you're miserable. But I can guarantee you you'll come through it. I'm not going to tell you to fake a smile or look on the bright side because I know when you're really down it feels so patronising. If you feel like you need to sob your heart out, then do by all means. You're well within your rights to be angry or upset – no one ever said it was an easy thing to have to come to terms with.

Bear in mind that you will get past this stage eventually, how-ever quickly or slowly it happens. You'll know for yourself when it's time to move on. And once you have started to accept this as nor-mality, you will be able just to get on with your everyday life.

Another thing that has changed so much for me in the space of a year is the way that I used to be so insecure with telling people about my diabetes. Earlier on I would have been mortified if any-one knew about it, but now I don't mind. If anyone wants to know anything about it then I'll happily answer their questions – I'd much rather they knew about diabetes than went off telling people incor-rect information based on badly-informed theories they may have invented.

My advice to anyone who doesn't feel ready to tell people is just not to force yourself into saying anything you're uncomfortable with. You will probably find that you don't want anyone else to know about your diabetes until you've started to come to terms with it yourself. But, again, you will come out of this phase eventually, and you will feel ready to talk more openly about everything. It may take a little push to start it off; if it feels more like pressure from other people then it's still probably too soon to blurt it out, but if you know that it's coming from within you and you don't really feel the need to keep it a secret any more, then go for it.

The same goes for moving on in general. You'll probably have worries that are different to the ones I had – everyone reacts differ-ently to situations. If you don't find it as much of a big deal as other people do then that's okay. On the other hand, if you feel it upsets you much more than it does other people, that's okay as well. We're all different – some of us get more emotional about things than oth-ers but it doesn't mean we're any worse or better people. It's just the way we are.

Life would be boring if we were all exactly the same.

On this planet there are short people, tall people, young peo-ple, old people; and there are also more than a million people who are type 1 diabetic. I happen to be one of them. But do you know what I say? I say yes, I have got diabetes, but so what? I am here and I am alive and I am well.

Life is for living, diabetes or not. Diabetes isn't a problem if you can look at it in the right way. It's an obstacle to be overcome – and, whether it be a mountain or a molehill, every obstacle has a way around it.

Diabetes isn't an illness. If it was an illness then I would be ill. I am not ill; I am well. Diabetes is a condition. A condition is just a part of your existence, something that goes on in your life. Would you describe a heavy cold as a condition? Okay, it's temporary, but it's still something that affects you. And I can say for almost certain that in a year or so, once you have come to terms with your diabetes, a bunged up nose and sinus headache will be *much* more annoying than a glucose meter and a few needles. Honestly.

Diabetes is what you make it. It isn't a particularly pleasant thing, and it's not a particularly easy thing to cope with either. But you can exaggerate it to an astronomical degree if you really want to. Or you can shrink the problem to the size of an ant. A positive frame of mind works wonders. It may not come naturally to begin with, but once you start to accept your diabetes as a part of your life, a reformed, happier attitude towards it will follow. I'm not suggesting that you're ever going to love the fact that you have diabetes, but you can accept it and get on with your everyday life without it bothering you. Just as the novelty of a new computer game or haircut wears off, so does the scariness of the idea of having diabetes for the rest of your life. It's what you get used to, isn't it?

If at the moment you can't imagine your life carrying on as normal in a year's time, don't worry too much about it. When you are first diagnosed it's understandable to have a kind of tunnel vision when you look to the future. Your life is probably so surreal and pan-icked that you almost forget the bits between your injections and blood tests. You forget that there's a person inside you hiding behind your diabetes. You just want to get on with a normal life, but you forget what a normal life is. I still remember what it feels like, a year on. I doubt I will forget it even in 50 years time. I don't feel trapped like that anymore, though. I am living a normal life.

Having said that, what is normal? Everyone is different – normal is an abstract concept. Somewhere between Joe Public and Marvin the Martian is a grey area that most of us fit into. Even people with diabetes.

But forget normal; I'm more interested in happy. Content. In other words, not crying everyday over things you can't change. Not literally beating yourself up because something inside you has killed off part of your pancreas. Not feeling angry and bitter towards anything that reminds you of your imperfections.

Science is moving forward all the time. You never know, one day in the future there might be a cure for diabetes. One day we might all be able to say, "Yes, I used to have diabetes" – and mean it. At some point in the future, it could happen.

Nonetheless, while the search for a cure goes on, so do our lives. We *are* still here, and we should make the most of it.

I have my whole life ahead of me. I'm not going to waste it. I fully intend to live to the best of my ability – diabetes or no diabetes. I can't say I like this condition. But neither can I say that I waste any of my energy on hating it. It's there. I know it's there. But it won't go away however much I cry or shout or silently curse it. So why bother? Life's too short. I've got used to my diabetes, and accepted it as part of normality. Now the rest of my life is ahead of me. I want to enjoy it. Even with diabetes. And I'm not going to waste any more of my time resenting it – because that's so last year…

Glossary

Aqueous humour – fluid that fills the chamber of the eye

Beta cells – the cells in the Islets of Langerhans of the pancreas which produce the hormone insulin

Carbohydrate – a substance with a complex molecular structure made up of different sugars which can be broken down into glucose inside the body

Coeliac disease – A condition which means intolerance to gluten, a substance found in foods containing wheat, oats barley and rye

Dextrose – a simple sugar; the form of sugar found in honey

Dialysis – the extraction of harmful substances from the blood if the kidneys are not working properly

Glucose – a simple sugar

Glucose meter – a device used to measure blood glucose levels

Glycaemic Index (G.I.) – a ranking of foods in order of how they affect blood glucose levels

Glucagon – hormone that raises blood sugar levels

HBA1c test – a blood test that shows how much glucose binds to red blood cells and gives a measure of the average blood glucose levels for the previous two to three months. The result is given as a percentage of blood haemoglobin to which the glucose is attached

Honeymoon phase (remission phase) – a phase beginning shortly after diagnosis, usually lasting between four months and a year, where insulin requirements are lower because the beta cells temporarily recuperate and increase insulin production. (N.B. not everyone with type 1 diabetes has a honeymoon phase)

Hyperglycaemia (hyper) – higher than normal blood sugar

Hypoglycaemia (hypo) – lower than normal blood sugar

Insulin – a hormone that lowers blood sugar levels by opening the door of the body's cells to allow glucose to go in. It is necessary to allow glucose from food to be used in the body's cells in order to provide energy and stay alive

Ketoacidosis – a state where the blood becomes acidic due to a high level of ketones when there is a lack of insulin

Ketones – a waste chemical that is created when the body turns fat into energy (ketones are poisonous in high concentrations)

Lancer – a device used to push the lancet into the skin to take a blood sample

Lancet – a small needle used to prick the finger to take a sample of blood

Lipodistrophy (lumps) – lumps of excess subcutaneous fat caused by injecting insulin repeatedly into the same site

Long-acting insulin – a background insulin that is given once a day, and which continues working for the full 24 hours

mmol/l (millimols per litre) – units used for measuring blood glucose levels

Multiple-injection regime – an insulin regime with four or five injections per day, using a basal long-acting insulin and a dose of short-acting or rapid-acting insulin with each meal. This treatment is most common for teenagers and adults

Neuropathy – nerve damage as a complication of diabetes after years of high sugar levels

Pancreas – an organ in the abdomen that produces insulin and glycogen, as well as other hormones and digestive enzymes

Rapid-acting insulin – insulin that works quickly for a short period of time, and that is usually given with a meal

Retinopathy – damage to the blood vessels at the back of the eye – a complication of diabetes that can occur after many years of high blood sugar levels

Starch – complex carbohydrates that take longer to be converted into glucose than sugars

Subcutaneous – under the skin

Twice-daily insulin regime – an insulin regime with two injections per day, each a combination of rapid-acting and intermediate-acting insulin. This treatment is more common among younger children

Type 1 diabetes – the type of diabetes where the pancreas has stopped producing insulin, and which is treated by insulin injections

Type 2 diabetes – the type of diabetes where the body has become resistant to the insulin it produces, and which is treated by oral medication, maintaining a healthy diet and sometimes by insulin injections too

Units (U) – Universal Insulin Units – a measure of insulin

Useful resources

Websites

- Diabetes UK website (www.diabetes.org.uk)
- Juvenile Diabetes Research Foundation website (www.jdrf.org.uk)

Books

- Type 1 Diabetes in Children, Adolescents and Young Adults (Third edition) by Dr Ragnar Hanas. Published by Class Publishing in 2006. 392 pages.

Index